50 YEARS
IN NUCLEAR POWER

A RETROSPECTIVE

50 YEARS
IN NUCLEAR POWER

A RETROSPECTIVE

SALOMON LEVY

American Nuclear Society
La Grange Park, Illinois USA

Library of Congress Cataloging-in-Publication Data

Levy, Salomon.
  50 years in nuclear power : a retrospective / Salomon Levy.
     p. cm.
  ISBN 0-89448-573-3
  1. Nuclear engineers—Biography. 2. Mechanical engineers—Biography. 3. Levy,
Salomon—Biography. 4. Nuclear energy—United States—History. 5. Nuclear
industry—United States—History. I. Title. II. Title: Fifty years in nuclear power.

  TK9014.L48A3 2007
  621.48—dc22
                              2007006929

                                                  ISBN: 0-89448-573-3
                         Library of Congress Catalogue Card Number: 2007006929
                                             ANS Order Number: 690075

                                      © 2007 American Nuclear Society
                                         555 North Kensington Avenue
                                         La Grange Park, Illinois 60525 USA

              Production: Quantum Publishing Services, Inc., Bellingham, WA, USA
                                          Typography: Kate Weisel
                                 Printed in the United States of America

Cover photo credits:
Top: Three Palo Verde nuclear power plants. Courtesy of Arizona Power Services.
Bottom: Dresden Nuclear Power Station (Dresden 1 in Sphere). Courtesy of Exelon Nuclear.

The author was associated with Dresden 1 Nuclear Power Plant starting in 1959 and ended his
association with Palo Verde Nuclear Power Stations in December 2004.

CONTENTS

PREFACE

I received my B.S. from the University of California at Berkeley in 1949 and I have had the opportunity to practice engineering for more than 50 years in a variety of nuclear power fields and positions. With the passing of years, the workload has decreased, as it should, after "retirement." So, a decision was made to write a retrospective of my engineering career because those years were exhilarating and fascinating and involved a variety of engineering work, including research, development, design, manufacturing, management, and consulting. The output of that engineering contributed to the satisfactory performance of many nuclear power plants, which produce 20 percent of the United States' electricity. My involvement, however, was also subject to challenging conditions: competitive pressures, changing regulations, cost overruns, order cancellations, and debates about safety risks, environmental impacts, proliferation, security, and sustainability.

Initially, it was doubtful that the retrospective would go to print because a new domestic nuclear plant had not been ordered for about thirty years. A nuclear power renaissance, however, is under way. In June 2006, NRG Energy announced its intention to build two General Electric 1,350-MWe advanced boiling water reactors at its South Texas Project site. Sixteen other electrical utilities are planning to build 26 new reactors across the United States, most using a new streamlined one-step (construction and operation) licensing process. The Nuclear Power 2010 Initiative is a $1.1 billion investment by the industry and the federal government to help the design and licensing of advanced passive light water reactors. The energy bill approved by Congress on July 29, 2005, provides a tax credit of up to $5.7 billion for the first six new nuclear plants as well as some $2 billion to cover legal challenges. In addition, the Department of Energy has proposed a Global Nuclear Energy Partnership (GNEP) that is expected to involve many nations committed to the nuclear option. GNEP seeks (1) to improve the utilization of uranium resources, (2) to reduce the need for geological repositories, and (3) to enhance nonproliferation. Those promising circumstances have encouraged me to publish my retrospective, hoping that it might help the design, construction, and operation of future reactors as well as encourage young engineers to enter the field of nuclear power and to participate in its anticipated resurgence.

This book consists of nine chapters. The first chapter covers the student years from my arrival in the United States in late 1945 to my departure from the University of California at Berkeley in 1953 to start my professional career with a Ph.D. in mechanical engineering. The second chapter deals with my first exposure to nuclear power at the Knolls Atomic Power Laboratory and during General Electric's entry into commercial nuclear power. In 1959, my involvement shifted to the development of boiling water reactors and Chapter 3 is devoted to that work up to 1966.

The management years extend from 1966 to 1977 and they are discussed in Chapters 4 and 5. Chapter 4 is devoted to engineering management, while Chapter 5 covers general management with responsibilities for other functions besides engineering. In late 1977, I resigned from General Electric. Many changes were happening at that time in the institutional framework and development of nuclear power. Chapter 6 gives a brief recounting of those changes in a desire to avoid their future recurrence and to provide an understanding of their impact on the economics and acceptance of nuclear power.

After leaving GE, I formed two consulting firms: S. Levy incorporated (SLI), which was sold in 1998, and Levy & Associates, of which I am the sole owner. The consulting years are covered in Chapters 7 and 8. They are not described as a function of time but by topical areas. Chapter 7 covers my direct consultations, while Chapter 8 is devoted to the role of the consulting firm SLI. Chapter 9 discusses how lessons learned during the retrospective might help the future growth of nuclear power and the involvement of new engineers who will be working in the nuclear industry.

Increased nuclear generation of electricity is needed to resolve the current U.S. energy crisis. We are in a crisis because "our demand for oil and natural gas is considerably in excess of our production and that imbalance is getting worse" (*Report of the National Energy Policy Development Group,* May 2001). "We should adopt and invest in the future approach to energy rather than the current borrowing from the future strategy" (R. H. Truly, *The Bridge,* Summer 2002). In addition to conservation and renewable resources, uranium and our large reserves in coal should be used to produce electricity, to develop another fuel for our transportation needs, and to reduce our dependence on foreign oil and natural gas.

Anecdotes, historical comments, and pictures are offered in Chapters 2 through 5 and 7 and 8 to break the monotony of an overly technical write-up. I realize that many may disagree with my recounting of events and evaluations, but this book is intended to record my views and it does. I hope other nuclear power veterans and young engineers involved in the revival of nuclear power enjoy it. For those not interested in the historical details, reading Chapter 9 may be enough. Also, the phrase "in retrospect" and italic lettering are used in Chapters 1 through 8 to identify critical issues and lessons learned. It is important to note that this write-up was prepared with the benefit of hindsight and that hindsight can help you see issues and patterns not obvious at the time they took place. Some of the comments may be overly complimentary, but this is to be expected.

Finally, I wish to express my appreciation to my wife Eileen who allowed me to go to the office to work on the book and to my daughter Linda Smith who helped with the typing and final editing. Also, I wish to recognize the efforts of Karen Vierow, the chairperson of the American Nuclear Society (ANS) Book Review Committee, and of the committee members for their comments and advice. Professor Vierow spent a considerable amount of time getting the book approved by ANS and I am very grateful for her continued support. Finally, I wish to thank Randall S. Bilof and Lorretta Palagi for their excellent editing work.

Salomon Levy
March 2007

ACRONYMS

ABWR	advance boiling water reactor
ACRS	Advisory Committee on Reactor Safeguards
AEC	Atomic Energy Commission
AECB	Atomic Energy Control Board
ALARA	as low as reasonably achievable
ALWR	advance light water reactor
ANL	Argonne National Laboratory
ANP	aircraft nuclear propulsion
ANS	American Nuclear Society
APED	Atomic Power Equipment Department
APS	American Physical Society
APS	Arizona Public Service
ASME	American Society of Mechanical Engineers
B&R	Brown & Root
B&W	Babcock & Wilcox
BNL	Brookhaven National Laboratory
BWR	boiling water reactor
C&I	control and instrumentation
CANDU	CANadian Deuterium natural Uranium
CBI	Chicago Bridge & Iron
CBIN	Chicago Bridge & Iron Nuclear
CE	Combustion Engineering
CHF	critical heat flux
CILC	crud-induced localized corrosion
COA	City of Austin
CSAU	code scaling applicability and uncertainty
DCH	direct containment heating
DOE	Department of Energy

EBR   experimental breeder reactor
EBWR   experimental boiling water reactor
ECCS   emergency core cooling system
EEI   Edison Electric Institute
EPRI   Electric Power Research Institute
ETR   Engineering Test Reactor
FOB   free on board
FSAR   Final Safety Analysis Report
GE   General Electric Company
GETAB   General Electric thermal analysis basis
GETR   General Electric Test Reactor
GIF   Generation IV International Forum
GNEP   Global Nuclear Energy Partnership
GORB   General Office Review Board
GPUN   General Public Utility Nuclear
GRNS   Gen IV Roadmap NERAC Subcommittee
H2TS   hierarchically two-tiered scaling
HRE   Homogeneous Reactor Experiment
HTGR   high-temperature gas reactor
IAEA   International Atomic Energy Agency
IAG   Industry Advisory Group
IE   Iowa Electric
INPO   Institute of Nuclear Power Operations
INSAG   International Nuclear Safety Advisory Group
ISEG   Independent Safety Evaluation Group
JCAE   Joint Committee on Atomic Energy
KAPL   Knolls Atomic Power Laboratory
KEPCO   Korea Electric Power Company
LBL   Lawrence Berkeley Laboratory
LLNL   Lawrence Livermore National Laboratory

LMFBR	liquid-metal fast breeder reactor
LOCA	loss-of-coolant accident
LOFT	loss-of-fluid test
LWR	light water reactor
MAAP	Modular Accident Analysis Program
MACE	melt attack and coolability experiment
MCHFR	minimum critical heat flux ratio
MIT	Massachusetts Institute of Technology
MSA	Mine Safety Appliances
MTR	Material Test Reactor
MWe	megawatt electrical
NCB	Nuclear Committee of the Board
NERAC	Nuclear Energy Research Advisory Committee
NFS	Nuclear Fuel Services
NOC	Nuclear Oversight Committee
NPSH	net positive suction head
NPT	Non-Proliferation Treaty
NRC	Nuclear Regulatory Commission
NRTS	National Reactor Test Station
NSAC	Nuclear Safety Analysis Center
NYU	New York University
OPG	Ontario Power Generation
ORNL	Oak Ridge National Laboratory
OSRC	Off-Site Review Committee
P&ID	process and instrumentation diagram
PCI	pellet-cladding interaction
PECO	Philadelphia Electric Company
PGCC	power generation control complex
PG&E	Pacific Gas and Electric

PIRT	phenomena identification and ranking technique
PP&L	Pennsylvania Power & Light
PRA	probabilistic risk assessment
PRTR	Plutonium Recycle Test Reactor
PSE&G	Public Service Electric and Gas
psi	pounds per square inch
PTS	pressurized thermal shock
Pu	Plutonium
PUREX	plutonium–uranium extraction
PWR	pressurized water reactor
QA	quality assurance
RASP	Reactor Analysis Support Package
RHR	residual heat removal
SIR	Sodium Intermediate Reactor
SLI	S. Levy Incorporated
SRE	Sodium Reactor Experiment
SSFI	safety system functional investigation
STP	South Texas Project
SWBR	simplified boiling water reactor
TMI	Three Mile Island
TPG	Technical Program Group
TRAC	Transient Reactor Analysis Code
TVA	Tennessee Valley Authority
UCB	University of California at Berkeley
UCLA	University of California at Los Angeles
VBWR	Vallecitos Boiling Water Reactor
VEPCO	Virginia Electric Power Company
WANO	World Association of Nuclear Operators

ONE

THE STUDENT YEARS

When I arrived in late 1945 in Philadelphia, I had a Moroccan passport and an immigration visa to finish my education. I applied to several engineering schools. My first choice was the Massachusetts Institute of Technology (MIT) because of its worldwide reputation, but MIT not only turned me down—it also lost my original transcripts from the Lycée Lyautey in Casablanca, Morocco. At the end of the Second World War, many GIs were returning home and taking advantage of the GI Bill to register at universities. They were given first priority—as they should have been—which explains my rejection by several technical colleges, including Carnegie Tech, Cal Tech, and Purdue. The only university willing to accept me was the University of California at Berkeley (UCB) but starting in the fall of 1946 and only if I enrolled as a foreign student paying an increased tuition fee until I could become a citizen (which normally would take five years). With no other available opportunity, it looked like the decision of where and when to go to college was being made for me rather than the other way around. So I set out to fill my time until September 1946 by taking classes at New York University (NYU), improving my ability to speak English, and being exposed to the business world by watching my oldest brother, Isaac, who was living in New York, complete international export-import transactions.

The NYU situation was comparable to that at other schools. The returning GIs had filled up all of the day courses and only night classes were open. I selected a freshman calculus class and it did not take long to notice the striking differences between the U.S. and French education systems. In the United States, the students were allowed to pick their own courses and did not have to attend all of the lectures. The amount of homework was minimal, and the results of midterm examinations were not announced orally so everyone knew the best and worst performers. The level of knowledge was also different. I had been exposed to calculus before and I was expected to memorize most of the integrals without having to look them up. The U.S. system placed more emphasis upon understanding the process, which I appreciated more and more over time. The final result was a grade A but, more importantly, I found it easy to follow the teacher and to absorb the course material.

English had been taken as a foreign language in high school. The teacher forced the students to only use English during classes and I found that I could manage dealing with the more mundane conversations during my long voyage from Casablanca to Philadelphia on a Liberty ship. To enhance my ability to speak English, I often went to movies and picked up numerous words of little value in my future engineering career. Most progress was achieved when I decided to think in English rather than translate the thoughts from French to English. Today, I still have trouble with words that use the diphthong *th* like *the* or *think,* but I do not have an obvious accent. Instead, my French has deteriorated and is much more deliberate while I search for the right French words to translate from English. *Vive la différence!*

My brother Isaac was in the export-import business. The business consisted of selling goods, particularly textiles, from the United States and buying back foreign products such as spices from other countries. It was done by telegram and the messages were coded to avoid leaks to competition. The process appeared simple. The customers were informed about what was available and the selling price and the potential delivery date. A transaction was completed when there was a match between a buyer's needs and a vendor's offer. Completion required adequate insurance and timely transportation, which was all done by ship in those days.

Another important issue was to keep the money involved to a minimum by issuing a letter of credit to the vendor and having the imported goods reach you free on board (FOB). It was also necessary to receive customer payment shortly after delivery. This made it look easy and I began to wonder why several more years of education were necessary. However, there were risks as in any other business. For example, when the quality of some of the arriving goods was inferior, checking their status at the source point became necessary. Also, in the case of black pepper two years later, when demand exceeded supply and prices kept rising, it was a shock to find out that a supplier had sold his stock of black pepper several times to take advantage of escalating prices. Fortunately, when it was time to deal with the credibility of that supplier, it was also time to go back to California and to have my more experienced brother resolve the problem. *In retrospect, several years later, it was interesting to note that quality assurance and credibility were just as important in engineering work.*

> In retrospect, several years later, it was interesting to note that quality assurance and credibility were just as important in engineering work.

The train trip on the *City of San Francisco* in the fall of 1946 took about three days and I was amazed by the size of my new country. My eyes remained glued to the windows as the landscape kept changing. San Francisco, somewhat because of its location on the Pacific Ocean, resembled Casablanca, which was a Moroccan harbor on the Atlantic Ocean. Upon arrival, I reported to the Administration Building where the housing personnel encouraged me to stay at the university dormitories in Richmond because the dormitories at Berkeley were full. The Richmond dorms were temporary wooden structures that had been used during the war by workers assembling Liberty ships. Campus transportation was by bus and the buses ran often enough to make the trip tolerable.

When I met with my adviser, there was another surprise. The engineering class was so large that it became necessary to enroll me in the College of Chemistry. The impact of that switch was minimal because many of the preparatory classes were applicable to either college. I was assured that I could reapply to the College of Engineering a year later as long as my grades were good enough. I enrolled for the maximum number of allowable class units and set out about a year late to become an U.S. engineer.

The GIs returning from the war had seen friends and enemies die in the fields of combat. They worked hard and were eager to graduate without making waves. I tried to meld with my classmates and went as far as adopting their disdain for the "rah-rah" cheerleading at football games where they responded with the middle finger raised in unison to express their opinion. The local sports writers were incensed enough to suggest a breakup of the university's entirely male rooting section. They did not understand that the postwar students were not willing to accept a program losing nine out of ten football games.

> In retrospect, correct physics may be the most important element of predicting the performance and safety of nuclear power plants.

This protest, including the burning of the coach in effigy and a few wooden stadium benches at the end of the season, was a new experience for me because I had been taught to control my opinion and not to react to slurs during the Nazi occupation years of Morocco.

During the first year, I spent most hours studying and getting good grades. In the fall of 1947, I was allowed to switch to mechanical engineering and to apply for a waiver of the extra tuition fee required from foreign students. In the spring of 1948, I took my first course in heat transfer from Professor Martinelli. He was an excellent teacher. His lectures and examinations emphasized *understanding of the prevailing mechanisms or "physics." In retrospect, correct physics may be the most important element of predicting the performance and safety of nuclear power plants.* Even though Professor Martinelli died while teaching that course, there is no question that he had a major influence upon my choice of major. Professor Seban finished teaching the course and my disappointment was so great that I read the newspaper sports section during the last few lectures. UCB had developed a strong capability in the fields of heat transfer and fluid flow in its attempts to counterbalance MIT in the East. I still have my *Berkeley Heat Transfer Notes* written by Boelter, Cherry, Johnson, and Martinelli because they can be quite useful for reference purposes and lectures. Boelter had just left Berkeley to become the dean of engineering at the University of California at Los Angeles (UCLA), while Martinelli was getting high praise for his work on liquid metal heat transfer and two-phase flow (gas–liquid and steam–water). Also, Professors Drake and Seban had received a contract to study heat transfer to boundary layers which formed around airfoils, and Professor Schaaf and his team were becoming leaders in high-altitude, low-pressure flows.

What I liked most about Berkeley was that I was left alone and that there appeared to be very little interest in my performance. That situation changed in the spring of 1948 when I took a course in thermal power engineering from Professor Johnson. To avoid demoralizing his students, he had developed an ingenious way to raise their scores in tests by allowing them to exceed 100. I made the mistake of getting 110, which increased the attention I received thereafter. *In retrospect, it is clear that the professors were evaluating their students early to determine which ones should be encouraged to go to graduate school.* [In fact, Professor Johnson became my adviser on my master of science (M.S.) thesis.] My influence at the Richmond dormitories was also growing and barbecues and volleyball matches were organized. Beer was provided to liven up the tournament, which it did. Alcohol, however, was then not allowed within one mile of university property and the dean of students asked me to visit him. Fortunately, he only gave me a warning because of my past good behavior and grades. He appeared to be glad that I did not possess just an all-work personality. At about the same time, I was invited to join a fraternity. With my last name, it was obviously a Jewish fraternity. When I visited their facility, it was easy to find out that their interest was in my grades rather than any aspect of my personality. They were disappointed by my refusal.

After nearly two full years of study, I returned to New York for the summer of 1948 when my brother Isaac gave me a job to earn some money for my senior year at Berkeley. I also attended Columbia University to satisfy graduation requirements for American history. The course dealt exclusively with U.S. history and practically did not touch upon the rest of the world in contrast to my previous historical studies, which covered many more world events and countries.

Upon my return to Berkeley, I took enough class units to graduate in the fall of 1949, including an advanced course in boundary layer heat transfer taught by Professor Seban. Seban's lecture material was original and at the edge of technology and my opinion about him and his ability changed considerably. Throughout that year, I was encouraged to attend graduate school at Berkeley and was offered assistant teaching and research positions to cover my expenses. Just to recover from my disappointment in 1946, I decided to apply at MIT where I was accepted. Before leaving Berkeley, I attended the graduation ceremonies and had my picture taken in cap and gown. After much retouching of the picture by the photographer—to improve my looks!—I sent it to my mother who was thrilled because she was the force behind having the youngest of her seven children go to college and get a degree.

I had been given the impression by the MIT mechanical engineering office that there would be a teaching assistant position for me when I reported, but that was not the case. The alternate was to apply for a scholarship. When the scholarship was denied and a loan was offered instead, I decided to return to Berkeley where I was assured of part-time work by telephone. So, after two weeks of confusion at MIT and of debate with my landlady about the Yankees and Red Sox, I was back in Berkeley. *In retrospect,* that *switch determined the course of my future engineering career because it allowed me to change from a major in textiles* at MIT, as suggested by my brothers, *to one in my favorite subject of heat transfer and fluid flow. To this day, I believe it was pure luck!*

It did not take too long to feel back at home at Berkeley. Half of the time was devoted to studying and the other half working as a research assistant on boundary layer flow. The laminar boundary layer flow conservation equations were well established and it was only a matter of obtaining answers for different assumptions and boundary conditions. In those days, the solutions were derived using a Friden mechanical calculator (a machine which, when inadvertently asked to divide by zero, would go on and on until it destroyed itself). *In retrospect,* I continue to look at that part of my career with envy because there was only one correct solution to the assumptions made. *There were no extraneous considerations due to cost, regulatory, risk, safety, and environmental issues.* Also, by carrying out tests in a wind tunnel, the analytical predictions could be checked in a short span of time. *Experimental uncertainty was the only issue* and it required the wind tunnel data to be obtained at night to reduce the temperature changes prevailing during daylight.

In retrospect, a return to the old review standards would ensure originality and reduce the exponential growth of technical literature.

From 1949 to 1953, six boundary layer articles were submitted for publication in technical journals in which I participated. In those days, the review of technical papers was much more stringent than today, with emphasis placed upon assurance that the material was original and not published previously. Today, it is much more common to see the same paper with minor changes presented at several different technical society meetings. Also, some of the listed coauthors have little to do with the results being presented. *In retrospect, a return to the old review standards would ensure originality and reduce the exponential growth of technical literature.*

After the war, the number of graduate students had increased, which allowed more friendships to develop and more get-togethers to be organized. Relationships with the professors evolved and they were now willing to have morning coffee and to join in bowling matches with their students. Some of those friendships have lasted for many years beyond Berkeley. Up to July 2003, I often saw Bill Clabaugh who graduated in 1949 when I did. We planned to play golf together only a few weeks before his recent death. Jim Hartnett was another long-time friend and a Ph.D. student of Professor Seban. His wife and my future wife were trying to learn how to play bridge at the YWCA, and I met my wife Eileen when a foursome was organized at her apartment to play cards. Also, I remember Jim's and my first game of golf in the Berkeley Hills with Bill Clabaugh who was a good golfer. As Jim's score and mine kept soaring, we decided to drink beer. His game improved due to his Irish ancestry, while mine kept getting worse.

In 1951, I had my first exposure to two-phase flow when I met Abou-Sabe, an Egyptian student sent to study agriculture, but trying to get his Ph.D. by measuring heat transfer to air–water mixtures under Professor Johnson. I suggested that an analytical solution to an idealized annular two-phase geometry could be obtained by assuming velocity profiles within the outer liquid annulus and the central gas core. In addition, the gas and liquid velocity were assumed to be equal at the interface. That model became the subject of my M.S. thesis and it was presented as a paper at the 2nd Midwestern Conference on Fluid Mechanics in 1952. Over the years, I have come back to that model several times because, although the first attempt reproduced the nondimensional parameters derived by Martinelli, it did not agree with the available test results. In 1966, that difficulty was resolved by using the enlarged amount of available test data to formulate an interface empirical correlation for friction. Subsequently, Professor Wallis showed that the1966 proposal was equivalent to his accepted relation for annular interfacial friction. In 1981, there was one more try to improve the model by showing that it was impossible for the liquid and gas to have the same velocity at the interface. Waves occurred at that location and their formation and shape determined the friction and the amount of entrained liquid in the gas core. This short sidetrack in annular flow is included to show that my contributions to the technical literature were not the result of flashes of brilliance but rather persistence and hard work. It also confirms that my technical involvement was able to overcome several extensive and sometimes difficult periods of managerial assignment. *In retrospect, I kept finding the time to stay abreast of the literature and to participate.*

In 1951 Eileen and I were married. When our daughter Linda was born about one year later, the pressure to complete my Ph.D. degree rose considerably and I selected the familiar topic of laminar boundary layer with large temperature changes for my thesis subject. By employing a new transformation and an integral form of the temperature variation, it became possible to make the boundary layer equations tractable and to use a differential analyzer to solve them. While completing that work, I only applied for a teaching position at Berkeley because it was my overwhelming choice for a long-term career. I expected that my production of several publications in less than three years would lead to an assistant professorship. To my great surprise, the chairman of the Mechanical Engineering Department felt that I was too much of a Berkeley inbred and offered me a lecturer position with no assurance of permanency unless I got other professional experience. My response was to deal with that issue right there and then. I secured an offer to work in the fall of 1953 for the Lawrence Livermore National Laboratory (LLNL) in Livermore, California, thanks to the help of Berkeley professors consulting for that laboratory. That arrangement satisfied my wife's great desire to stay in Northern California.

After spending all of our money on a well-deserved vacation at Lake Tahoe, I reported to Lawrence Livermore and was told on my first day of work that the contract I was hired for had been canceled. I was given two weeks' notice and a problem to solve during that time span. I drove back home and upon entering the house, my wife's joking comment was "What happened, did you get fired?" "Right on" was my reply and I immediately got on the phone to obtain another job offer. My first call was to Bob Brooks who had tried several times to get me to go to the Knolls Atomic Power Laboratory (KAPL). I explained my situation and indicated that I needed an offer within two weeks. He arranged for three interviews at General Electric and I accepted his generous offer because I knew him personally. Within two weeks the family was packed and on the way to Schenectady, New York, in an old used Studebaker. Believe it or not, I never provided Lawrence Livermore a reply to their assigned problem!

During the slow trip from Berkeley to Schenectady and a few times thereafter, I have reflected about my shattered dream of an academic career and the unanticipated thrust into commercial nuclear power away from California. The future might have been quite different but I never dwelled too long on it once I got involved in my work in industry. The result was a fifty-year career in nuclear power!

TWO

THE INITIAL YEARS

Upon arrival in Schenectady, the engine in the old Studebaker had to be replaced because the head cracked just beyond Cleveland, Ohio. Also, rental housing was not easy to find and the furniture arriving from Berkeley had to be stored in a warehouse. Fortunately, a lease for a newly completed house in Scotia, New York, was signed shortly after the willingness to pay premium rates was advertised in the local newspaper. When I reported to work, I was located in a temporary building away from the Knolls Atomic Power Laboratory (KAPL), while waiting for my Q clearance. In the meantime, to keep me busy, I was authorized to attend a technical meeting in Buffalo, New York, to become familiar with current nuclear programs. My wife agreed, while I was gone, to handle the moving of the furniture from the warehouse and she was flabbergasted to find out that my signature was required to release the stored goods. California community property law apparently had not yet reached upstate New York.

While attending the Buffalo meeting, I realized that my knowledge about nuclear reactors was close to zero. Once overnight, I had operated the liquid metal heat transfer loop sponsored by KAPL, known as "the Knolls," at Berkeley and I had measured heat transfer coefficients above any reported previously. Professor Johnson spent considerable time trying to explain and reproduce that anomaly, but to no avail.

Also, I became aware of the Aircraft Nuclear Propulsion (ANP) program when I interviewed with General Electric and declined their offer to join them, against the advice of the dean of engineering, because of misgivings about their mission.

My first work problem at the Knolls was to analyze the cooling required to freeze plugs rotating within a thin hot liquid metal annulus. The amount of cooling required was several times the predicted value because it had been assumed that the hot liquid metal would rise along the outer surface of the annulus while the cooled liquid metal would flow down along the inner surface. In fact, nearly square natural circulation cells occupying the entire annulus were forming and interacting up and down with adjoining cells to increase the flow rate and the degree of cooling required. A test verified that pattern, and the solution was to add wires along the circumference at different vertical levels to increase the number of cells, reduce their size, and the cooling they produced. My contribution was to develop a methodology to predict natural circulation for different configurations including inclined plates, across cylinders, and within pipes and annuli. That report and its subsequent publication in the *Journal of Applied Mechanics* led to my being asked to write a natural circulation chapter in the *Liquid Metal Handbook*. That gave me my first and only opportunity to meet Admiral Hyman G. Rickover. I was attending a review of the handbook at Mine Safety Appliances (MSA) in Pittsburgh when I was offered a ride to the train station to get back to Schenectady. The Admiral was in town at the same time, observing the impact of failing piping containing highly pressurized water, and he needed a ride to the same railroad station. When he arrived, there was a curt hello and he sat in the front seat and asked for the inside light to be kept on while he worked through the entire ride reading material in his briefcase.

The next assignment was to predict the natural circulation in steam generators. Using a simplified expression for steam slip in saturated water developed by Professor Rohsenow of MIT, the calculated value nearly matched the measurements in full-scale prototype tests. *In retrospect,* what impressed me most during that first year at the Knolls, *were the Naval Reactor Branch's strategies of avoiding performance surprises and their insistence on getting the right answers from full-scale tests. The construction of a complete pressurized water submarine prototype at the National Reactor Test Station (NRTS) at Idaho and of a full liquid metal prototype at West Milton, New York, and its location within a spherical containment are memorable examples of that management objective and of the importance assigned to safety.*

When the Admiral and his top lieutenants visited the Knolls, the relevant issues were defined, attendance was specified, and considerable staff work was carried out ahead of the meeting to facilitate decision making. Even at my low level in the organization, you could feel the electricity in the air during those periodic visits, and anybody who was not involved was instructed to stay away. Sometimes, there was noticeable tension between the Admiral and the highest levels of General Electric management who were maneuvering for authority to select and replace Knolls managers. *In retrospect, there is no question that nuclear power was the perfect application for submarine propulsion and that the entire U.S. government system always supported and enthusiastically funded it. (That condition unfortunately did not extend long enough for commercial nuclear power generation.)*

> In retrospect, what impressed me most were the Naval Reactor Branch's strategies of avoiding performance surprises and their insistence on getting the right answers from full-scale tests.

When questions arose about the use of a liquid metal for coolant aboard the submarine *Seawolf,* the joking response attributed to the Admiral was that General Electric (GE) would have invented a water-cooled reactor if the oceans were made up of liquid sodium. In fact, GE had an early interest in pursuing a fast liquid metal–cooled breeder reactor, but research funds could not be secured for its development. At that same time, the Naval Reactor Branch was concerned about the reliability and failure of components operating with highly pressurized water. As a backup, a low-pressure reactor cooled by sodium was selected and it utilized an intermediate neutron spectrum between fast and thermal to improve its safety. Another type of liquid metal reactor was operational at Idaho, the Experimental Breeder Reactor No. 1 (EBR-1), which reached full power in 1951. EBR-1 used sodium/potassium for coolant and was dedicated to illustrating the feasibility of breeding. The much larger Sodium Intermediate Reactor (SIR) at Knolls emphasized reliable power production, particularly from its reactor and its saturated water and superheated steam heat exchangers. More than 20 heat exchange configurations were tested and over 90 percent of those models failed due to excessive combined pressure and thermal stresses across the tubes (KAPL-1450). The problem was aggravated by the very late decision not to allow mercury aboard submarines. Mercury had been chosen as an intermediate fluid between water/steam and sodium because it is an inert fluid which does not react with them. That was not the case with the sodium/potassium (NaK) mixture selected to replace mercury. NaK reacts with water or steam to produce stress corrosion of austenitic stainless steel. The *Seawolf* superheat unit failed shortly after going to sea. That failure and the excellent performance of the pressurized water reactor (PWR) aboard the *Nautilus* led the Navy to abandon the Knolls strong program for liquid metal to water/steam heat exchangers. *In retrospect, the reliability and costs of liquid metal equipment to produce saturated and superheated steam are still the most important issues for the success of liquid metal–cooled thermal and fast reactors.*

Shortly after that interesting start at KAPL, the decision was made to split a separate group of engineers away from the Knolls to design and purchase submarine equipment especially for the balance of plant. I was transferred into that group. My first assignment was to develop a model to predict the level swell in the *Seawolf* steam/water pressurizer. The predicted level swell was never validated because the group was separated from the Knolls once Admiral Rickover heard of ongoing work about boiling water reactors (BWRs). I was assigned then to non-naval studies and I lost my clearance. I found out about my loss of clearance when some Knolls engineers wanted my advice about boiling heat transfer. The meeting they requested had to be held in the Knolls cafeteria because I no longer had a Q clearance.

General Electric had made a proposal to Kaiser Engineers to design the core and controls for the Engineering Test Reactor (ETR). The ETR was to provide larger experimental spaces and irradiation fluxes than the

Materials Test Reactor (MTR). It was to be located next to the MTR at the Idaho Test Station, which was then being run by Phillips Petroleum Co. When Kaiser Engineers was selected for the contract, the experienced GE engineers who had prepared the proposal were busy working on commercial nuclear power projects and a "green" team inherited the test reactor design work. I was put in charge of thermal hydraulics and licensing even though I had no reactor engineering experience. Similarly, Bert Wolfe, a recent physics Ph.D. from Cornell University, took over nuclear reactor analysis, and Jerry Jacobson managed the mechanical reactor design work even though they also had limited prior experience. During the project duration, Phil Bush, the project manager for Kaiser Engineers, kept teasing us about the disappearance of the top GE engineers who had prepared the proposal and had made the presentations to secure the contract.

The "green" team, however, performed very well by getting familiar with the design of the MTR and extrapolating it to the more difficult ETR conditions. The continued assistance of Phillips Petroleum engineers was especially helpful. In the thermal-hydraulics area, a test facility was built at Schenectady, New York, to study the pressure differential across the thin aluminum fuel plates and to measure the heat transfer rate in a small rectangular channel formed by electrically conducting flat plates. Figure 2.1 is a picture of the facility control panels with the author dressed to look his best. Educational Services of General Electric took advantage of that facility and my role in its design and construction to encourage young engineering graduates to join GE. As might be expected, the advertisement embellished my participation so as to have the greatest impact upon college students. During the Engineering Test Reactor startup test, there was an urgent phone call asking for the facility to be shipped to Idaho because some fuel plates were damaged during the preliminary flow runs. *In retrospect,* it was found that the dummy fuel plates being tested at Schenectady had been cold-worked by straightening them. *That minor departure from prototypic conditions was an important*

> In retrospect, that minor departure from prototypic conditions was an important lesson learned.

lesson learned. Fortunately, it provided the answer to the problem, that is, cold-working the actual fuel plates.

There was one other important disagreement during the project and it dealt with the selection of the inlet water temperature to the reactor core. With downward flow into the core, it was important to avoid boiling and burnout (overheating) of the fuel, and an inlet temperature of 110°F was recommended to cover transients and accidents. Kaiser wanted to raise the inlet temperature to 130°F to save $200,000 in heat exchanger costs. A top-level meeting was scheduled to debate the issue and GE was asked to send another heat transfer expert to participate in the discussions. George Roy, a very good friend in later years, came from Hanford. The meeting was attended by Dr. Doan, director of the laboratory, and by several of his managers, as well as Phil Bush. A detailed presentation was made about the selected margin and a separate calculation, employing the Materials Test Reactor methodology, was offered to show that the inlet temperature would have to be reduced to match the MTR safety margin. Following a separate caucus by Phillips personnel, it was decided to accept the 110°F inlet temperature. That difference in position is touched on in the Nucleonics publication of March 1957, the cover of which is reproduced in Figure 2.2. It is discussed because it is the first of several subsequent disagreements between architect-engineers and reactor vendors. In the concluding paragraph about the ETR, Bush (Bush, P. D., *Nucleonics,* March 1957) states that "the advantage of using an architect-engineer as prime contractor for design and construction is quite clear: Such a firm can design and construct the most economical over-all facility without being tied to the products of any one manufacturer. It is also interesting to note that the reactor, the controls and instrumentation represent less than 20% of the over-all cost of the ETR." *Bush's statement about economical facility fails to recognize the importance of safety.* In retrospect, in the Engineering Test Reactor case, the total project cost was $17,200,000 and a saving of $200,000 (slightly more than 1 percent) in heat exchangers could not be justified with respect to the corresponding loss in fuel temperature safety margin. It is also important to note that nuclear steam supply systems in nuclear power plants account for less than 20 percent of the total plants' costs

What young people are doing at General Electric

Young engineer works on new ways to remove heat from atomic reactors

DR. SALOMON LEVY joined G.E. in 1953 after receiving his B.S. in M.E. from the Univ. of Calif. in 1949. In 1951 he received his M.S., and in 1953 his Ph.D. From '49-'50 he was teaching assistant at U. of C., and '50-'53 he was Junior Research Engineer at the Institution of Engineering Research.

An atomic reactor running at full efficiency creates a tremendous amount of heat in its core. By removing this heat and putting it to work boiling water to make steam, atom-made electricity is produced.

One of the men responsible for designing new, more efficient ways to remove heat from atomic reactors is 29-year-old Doctor Salomon Levy — Design Analysis supervisor in the Atomic Power Equipment Department's Reactor Engineering Unit.

Levy's Work Interesting, Vital

To study this problem of heat transfer, G.E. recently constructed a heat-transfer system. By electrically simulating the heat produced in a reactor, it is possible to determine the maximum rate at which heat can be removed from a reactor to make steam.

Dr. Levy conceived the idea of building this complex system, designed it and supervised its construction. At present, Levy works with this system to study new problems of heat transfer and fluid flow encountered in atomic power plants.

25,000 College Graduates at General Electric

When Salomon Levy came to General Electric in 1953, he already knew the kind of work he wanted to do. Like each of our 25,000 college-graduate employees, he was given his chance to grow and realize his full potential. For General Electric has long believed this: Whenever fresh young minds are given the freedom to make progress, everybody benefits — the individual, the company, and the country.

Educational Relations, General Electric Company, Schenectady 5, New York

Progress Is Our Most Important Product

GENERAL ⊕ ELECTRIC

Figure 2.1.   The author standing in front of GE ETR thermal-hydraulic facility control panels. (Source: GE advertisement, 1955)

while being responsible for most of their safety. They were subjected to similar pressure to reduce initial costs at the expense of long-term reliability, safety, and operating margins.

> In retrospect, today, the completion of design, construction, and licensing of such a complex facility in less than two years would be considered remarkable.

When the Engineering Test Reactor went critical in May 1957, two years had elapsed since the start of design and a year and a half since start of construction. The GE team performed within schedule even though it had to build a new facility with electrically heated parallel flat plates to determine burnout conditions and to develop three-dimensional system computer codes to predict neutron fluxes in the reactor core. *In retrospect, today, the completion of design, construction, and licensing of such a complex facility in less than two years would be considered remarkable. One reason was that the talented members of the Advisory Committee on Reactor Safeguards (ACRS) offered advice and participated in the resolution of problems and issues. Another reason was the lack of an extensive set of disjointed rules. Furthermore, there were no litigious public hearings and no intervention.*

In late 1953, President Eisenhower proposed the Atoms for Peace initiative (Eisenhower, D. D., *Nuclear News,* November 2003) and the congressional Joint Committee on Atomic Energy (JCAE) and the Atomic Energy Commission (AEC) set out to implement it vigorously. There were reactor development programs in place before the Atoms for Peace announcement (West, J. W., and Davis, W.K., *Nuclear News,* June 2001). They included the previously noted Experimental Breeder Reactor and the Homogeneous Reactor Experiment (HRE), which became operational in 1952 at Oak Ridge National Laboratory (ORNL). In 1954, the number of reactor experiments was expanded to include a pressurized water reactor at Shippingport, Pennsylvania; an Experimental Boiling Water Reactor (EBWR) at Argonne National Laboratory (ANL) in Chicago; a thermal Sodium Reactor Experiment (SRE) at Santa Susana, California; and larger versions of the EBR and HRE. Subsequently, there were several more rounds of request for small

Figure 2.2.   March 1957 *Nucleonics* cover. (Source: McGraw Hill, 1957)

demonstration nuclear power plants and most received development funds and fuel cost savings from the government.

GE top management seized upon that opportunity to enter the energy business and to use uranium instead of fossil fuel. A small study group was assembled at Schenectady to evaluate the role of GE. Their first proposal to Consolidated Edison consisted of a graphite-moderated reactor cooled by light water, patterned after the Hanford N production reactor. For cost reasons, a pressurized water reactor offered by Babcock & Wilcox (B&W) was selected instead. It used thorium fuel and a separate fossil superheat unit. GE then acquired the services of Sam Untermeyer from ANL. Sam was a strong proponent of the boiling water reactor and encouraged its adoption because of its potential cost advantage due to lack of steam generators. Agreement was eventually reached to supply a 200-MW BWR to Commonwealth Edison Company on a turnkey fixed-price basis. No government assistance was pursued. A total business plan was also generated and a new business site was selected. San Jose, California, was chosen because of its proximity to good universities and because California was expected to need nuclear power due to its stringent environmental requirements. As much as I agreed with the California location, I had no involvement in that choice. I was asked only about the Berkeley Engineering Field Station, located in Richmond, and I was negative because I remembered the presence of an adjoining sulfur plant when taking boundary layer data at that site. At that very short meeting, *there was also a mention of California earthquakes but their role was considered manageable.*

I still remember the business plan presentation to encourage engineers to move to the West Coast. It visualized an enormous growth in personnel and products. The plan called for 80,000 employees to cover all the forecasted business and they were located at different sites. To match that vision, GE agreed to build a laboratory at Vallecitos with a critical facility, hot cells, a test reactor, and a small Vallecitos Boiling Water Reactor (VBWR). Engineering facilities for fluid flow, heat transfer, corrosion, and control rod drive testing were to be located at San Jose. The AEC then estimated that nuclear generating capacity could be as high as 700,000 megawatts electrical (MWe) by the year

2000, or about seven times its actual value.

Those were the euphoric days of nuclear power generation (as described by Davis and West in the June 2001 issue of *Nuclear News*). Several reactor types were accepted for development without a critical review of their merits and without an independent assessment of their claim that they could compete with fossil power plants. *There was no sound comparative methodology for the selection of concepts under the AEC power demonstration program; some projects were initiated and never completed. The program also failed to recognize the large funding provided for naval applications and the progress they achieved. In retrospect, it is not surprising that water-cooled reactors became the dominant choice for U.S. nuclear power plants.*

There was no sound comparative methodology for the selection of concepts under the AEC power demonstration program.

Until the move to San Jose in 1956, the Engineering Test Reactor project occupied most of my time. There were a few opportunities to work on BWR and test reactors. For example, we were asked to prepare a proposal for three small natural circulation reactors to be located in Cuba. This led to an opportunity to visit the Experimental Boiling Water Reactor at ANL and to copy that design except for substituting low enriched uranium oxide (UO_2) fuel rods for metallic fuel plates. It is fortunate that Cuba could not afford to purchase nuclear power plants because their presence on that island would have raised different political issues during the ascension of Castro to power and the subsequent missile crisis.

Another instance was the use of a dual cycle in the Dresden-1 plant in Morris, Illinois, with part of the steam being generated in secondary steam generators. This feature allowed the plant to respond to load demand by increasing the steam produced in the secondary generators, decreasing the feed-water temperature, and raising the BWR power level. The same capability can be achieved by varying the reactor flow rate. A patent was filed for that concept and detailed analyses were provided to support it. *In retrospect, the variable flow invention made it possible to eliminate the secondary steam generators and the need to repair failed tubes during operation.* In another involvement with swimming pool test reactors, I suggested the use of natural circulation and the addition of a chimney above the core to eliminate the need for pumps to produce downward flow through the fuel. The only problem was increased radioactivity at the top of the pool. *In retrospect, that was my first initiation to ALARA (as low as reasonably achievable) and I never forgot that lesson: to look for unanticipated personnel exposures and eliminate them.*

Upon arrival in San Jose, I wanted to work on BWRs, but there was already a fully staffed project team working on Dresden-1. Instead, I agreed to join the Advance Engineering organization under Karl Cohen and to become more familiar with the power side of the business. Advance Engineering had just initiated a study of liquid metal–cooled plants with large power outputs. An advanced design was developed for a sodium-cooled power plant that was moderated with graphite and beryllium and used oxide fuel. The reactor core consisted of modules containing fuel and beryllium, surrounded with graphite and coupled by it to produce power. Each module was a sealed, structurally strong container having its own inlet and outlet sodium piping connections. That arrangement avoided the canning of graphite blocks and their reported failure in the Sodium Reactor Experiment and the subsequent Hallam (Nebraska) plant, but it required complex piping interconnections between the modules. That concept never went beyond the design stage.

> The purpose of Sunrise was to get power generators to sponsor small demonstration plants of the proposed novel options.

There was also an opportunity to assist with the formulation of the GE Sunrise Program. Sunrise identified several long-term options for development of the BWR. They included simplification and improvements in compactness, power density, and thermal cycle efficiency. *The purpose of Sunrise was to get power generators to sponsor small demonstration plants of the proposed novel options.* Their best features were to be combined into larger future offering of boiling water reactors. Sunrise also provided for *closing the fuel cycle by recycling plutonium in light water thermal reactors and eventually deploying breeder reac-*

tors to utilize their plutonium. The Atomic Energy Commission (AEC) was then fully supportive of that strategy.

The Sunrise program was not implemented as originally planned or scheduled. The simplified plant version was a natural circulation BWR with gravity steam separation in which Pacific Gas and Electric (PG&E) was interested. PG&E was also willing to sponsor tests of a novel pressure suppression containment system. That design quenched any steam/water mixture released accidentally from the reactor system into a pool of subcooled (below saturation temperature) water. Those features were incorporated in the Humboldt Bay (California) plant, which started operation in August 1963 and had an output of 63 MWe. Consumers Power Company selected the high power density option with a spherical dry containment for its Big Rock Point plant in Charlevoix, Michigan. It had a power output of 67 MWe and started operating in1964. Niagara Mohawk supported the construction of a superheat reactor at Vallecitos to improve the thermal cycle efficiency. That reactor and the comparable BONUS demonstration plant in Puerto Rico were shut down shortly after startup due to fuel cladding stress corrosion cracking. Compactness was first introduced at Oyster Creek (New Jersey); it used a variable-speed pump and internal steam separation. It became operational in 1969, reaching an eventual output of 650 MWe. *In retrospect, while several Sunrise features found their way into the BWR product line, the biggest contributor to cost reduction over the years was increasing power output and fuel exposure. Interestingly, that condition still prevails today.*

GE had formed a Safety Council and appointed Karl Cohen as its chairman. The council members were top engineers from other GE divisions, such as the steam turbine generator and aircraft jet engine divisions, and they met periodically to review new nuclear power plant proposals or significant changes in design or plant operation. I was secretary of the council and prepared the minutes. It was fascinating to observe the discussion and resolution of issues. It was difficult to get the minutes approved and recording the discussions did not help. Also, GE had developed its own model for release of fission products during severe accidents and it was used to calculate the potential consequences for proposal sites. *In retrospect, those risk studies did not allow a GE proposal to be made for the Ravenswood plant, which was to be located in the middle of New York City. It was never built.* Similarly, dual-pressure suppression containment was required for the Muehleberg plant sited in a highly populated part of Switzerland. Involvement with the council made it possible to track development and business progress. I found it especially rewarding when the council members allowed me to participate in a few discussions.

The rest of the time was spent providing consulting services to the organization, including helping with the licensing of the GE Test Reactor (GETR), analyses of the pressure suppression system and of the Vallecitos BWR containment pressure, and comparative cost evaluations of design concepts and fuel cycles. The challenge of paper studies was decreasing, and I agreed to consider joining the Princeton University faculty where Bob Drake was in charge of mechanical engineering. At that particular moment, the Dresden-1 plant design was being subjected to an intensive independent review. The report raised several important issues and the manager of engineering, Bob Richards, asked me to prepare the response and to determine the development work required. Also, I was given the opportunity to move to Development Engineering where I would be in charge of heat transfer and fluid flow development. Due to the perfect timing of that offer, I believe that the possibility of my leaving GE contributed to the new assignment. Six years after joining GE, I had the job I longed for and I accepted in spite of being impressed by the Princeton campus and faculty.

THREE

THE DEVELOPMENT YEARS

GE had the habit of conducting independent audits of a business or project when headquarters sensed that the risks were becoming excessive. The Dresden-1 plant reached that category because its power level was about 30 times the output attained in much smaller experimental plants. The audit report was highly critical. It identified concerns in the areas of fuel cladding burnout (excessive fuel cladding temperature), reactor core stability, fuel exposure, balance of plant radioactivity, and corrosion. The review team believed that it would be difficult to exceed 50 percent of warranted power and to achieve one-third to one-half of the planned fuel burnup of 10,000 megawatt-days per ton (MWd/ton). *In retrospect, during my 25 years at GE, I found that independent reviews seldom identified new issues. Still, their benefit was significant in that they increased management attention to problems, requiring an action plan to be developed along with periodic progress reports.*

In the case of the Dresden-1 audit, the response consisted of identifying the shortcomings that had been highlighted in the review report and turning them over to development personnel to determine the actions and programs to be carried out to alleviate their impact. *A multifunctional team,* including design personnel, reviewed the entire audit package and *took a first cut to have the demands for funds satisfy the increased available budget, which is not an unusual situation.* This was reviewed with development engineers to get their approval and their final changes. The end result was nearly a consensus report with practically no complaint to the manager of engineering. The result was to have my job expanded to review development plans to be carried out in subsequent years.

I assumed responsibility for two of the Dresden-1 critical issues: burnout and stability. In the case of stability, the responsibility was shared with the physics group because of the coupling between in-core steam voids and reactivity. The burnout situation was resolved in a very conservative manner. All of the available data for BWR conditions were plotted on a single graph of burnout heat flux versus steam quality at the operating pressure of 1000 pounds per square inch (psi) and a limit line drawn below all the test results. That limit line approach was adopted because the available information was very poor and the available data scatter was very large. In addition, a margin factor of 2 was provided at the worst reactor thermal location. That strategy gave us enough time to get applicable data and to improve the original limit line.

An annular geometry was selected for the GE tests because it was representative of the corner rod of the BWR fuel assembly and its surrounding Zircaloy channel. That rod produced the highest power of all the fuel rods due to its increased water moderation. In those early days, electrical current was conducted through the test rod, constant heat flux generation was employed, and burnout always occurred at the exit of the test section, which made it much easier to detect. Initially, it was difficult to preserve the spacing between the heated rod and the outer annulus. Ed Polomik, who was in charge of that work, eventually resolved that difficulty by installing small sapphire rods 120 degrees apart around the circumference at different axial levels. Because of consistency and repeatability of the newly generated data, the large scatter in the original limit line plot decreased. A good part of the scatter was due to combining circular and annular test data and the presence of unstable test loop results. In an annular geometry, more water accumulates on the cold outer wall, which increases the steam content along the heated rod and lowers its burnout value. A new correlation, called the Janssen-Levy limit line, and a reduction in safety margin were proposed and accepted.

In retrospect, the correct geometrical scaling and the use of conservatism to compensate for lack of full understanding had served GE well in the burnout area.

In retrospect, the correct geometrical scaling and the use of conservatism to compensate for lack of full understanding had served GE well in the burnout area.

Beyond that point, the work consisted of investigations in direct support of BWR designs and fundamental evaluations of two-phase flow and burnout, which was called now critical heat flux (CHF). The design work involved calibrating inlet orifices, measuring two-phase pressure drop in a prototypic fuel assembly operating at different constant steam qualities at full pressure, and in *determining the degree of fretting at the spacers and flow-induced vibrations.* In the case of CHF, data were obtained for four-rod and nine-rod geometries instead of a single-rod annulus, and the rod-to-rod and rod-to-channel spacing were varied. New Hench-Levy limit lines were developed to incorporate the latest information and to introduce mass flow rate as a parameter. It was recognized that the latest set of design curves had several shortcomings. For example, it was known that, in boiling water reactors, CHF was caused by depletion of the water film protecting the fuel rod surface and that such evaporation would depend on the rod-to-rod and axial power distribution. Also, fuel spacers could trip the water film and initiate CHF upstream of the spacer. Those uncertainties were provided for by again drawing the design curves below practically all available data for each mass flux and by applying a safety margin of 1.9 to the minimum critical heat flux ratio (MCHFR). The decision was then made to determine future thermal limits of BWRs from full-scale simulations of fuel assemblies. Also, to be able to study spacer performance, internally heated rods were used instead of direct electrical heat production. *In retrospect, after the full-scale facility went into operation and generated thousands of data points, GE-BWRs had the most accurate thermal analysis basis (GETAB) for avoiding CHF because the test data were fully representative of reactor geometry and conditions. The Naval Reactor Branch strategy of utilizing full-scale prototypic facilities had paid off again.*

In recent years, *I have become suspicious of exclusive data treatments by computers if they do not provide for the involved physics.* For example, with a large amount of data, such correlation formulations are dominated by the behavior in regions with the most data and may not represent conditions with limited data.

In the case of BWR stability, there were three primary considerations. The first one was assurance of overall plant stability, which meant that the reactor and turbine generator could work well together during load demands and other operational transients. At Dresden-1, this was accomplished by the use of a dual-cycle system and by a primary water flow control system in subsequent models. The other two areas of interest were first, the plain thermal-hydraulic stability within fuel channels and, second, the reactor core stability in response to nuclear feedback effects from changes in core steam content and fuel temperatures. The young and energetic team of Eric Beckjord and Wes Harker was assigned responsibility for resolving those remaining areas of concern.

Thermal-hydraulic oscillations had been observed before in electrically heated steam/water test facilities. Eric was able to generate them in the San Jose heat transfer loop when it was operated in a natural circulation mode at reactor pressure level. Those experiments helped to confirm the role of inlet subcooling and the importance of increasing the inlet orifice and reducing the ratio of two-phase to single-phase pressure drop along the fuel. Using a single point kinetic representation of the core, a multitude of reactor stability assessments were carried out to predict the high decay ratio (or damping) of Dresden-1 oscillations. However, the topic of core stability was not fully resolved because there was no operating data from cores as large as that at Dresden-1. The concern was whether several critical smaller cores could form and operate without being coupled to each other. Unfortunately, two- and three-dimensional nuclear-steam void models were not available to check coupling as a function of time and location. The decision was made then to monitor for such behavior during the Dresden-1 startup studies and to send the team of Beckjord-Harker to the site to get their guidance as the power was increased. There was only one Dresden-1 oscillation large enough to arouse the attention of the development oscillation team, but it was in the balance-of-plant area and with no connection to core stability. Over the years, periods of local power oscillations have occurred in BWRs when they were subjected to unanticipated performance levels or abnormal transients but they were self-limiting in amplitude and corrective actions could be taken to avoid them. *Dresden-1 core reached full power and remained stable during the entire power escalation program. In retrospect, first-of-kind nuclear power plants can validate their safety by carrying out a comprehensive start-up and power escalation test program.*

> In retrospect, first-of-kind nuclear power plants can validate their safety by carrying out a comprehensive start-up and power escalation test program.

Also, when I visited the plant, I had the opportunity to observe Phil Bray use the CHF limit lines and the monograms he had constructed to maintain the required safety thermal margins during plant operation. *The Dresden-1 Independent Review had met its objectives to hold down company risks. In fact, its impact was to be felt for many more years, as summarized next.*

An outstanding team of talented engineers was assembled, and they took turn improving the understanding of thermal-hydraulic phenomena relevant to BWRs. In alphabetical order, the team included Eric Beckjord, Garry Dix, Jim Healzer, John Hench, Earl Janssen, R. T. Lahey, Jr., Dick Niemi, Ed Polomik, Tony Schraub, Bill Sutherland, and Frank Tippetts. To put the caliber of these personnel in perspective, two of them had Ph.D. degrees when they joined GE and six others received their doctorate degrees from Stanford University or Berkeley, while working for or on short leave from GE. The quality of the studies was determined by the university advisers and all of the doctorate theses were creative enough to have them published and presented by the authors at technical society meetings.

Great strides were made in developing the fundamental conservation equations and their application to predict normal, transient, and accident conditions in BWRs. Original experimental and analytical work was carried out to determine the flow and steam void distribution within fuel assemblies. Most of those results were released in 1977 in a monograph prepared by R. T. Lahey, Jr., and F. J. Moody for the American Nuclear Society. Its perusal, which goes well beyond the scope of this write-up, will confirm that it provides an excellent compendium of the work initiated in 1959 and carried out for many years thereafter. The monograph also offers an excellent description of the GE BWR and its safety systems as well as of the important work of Fred Moody in the areas of critical flow and containment design. A comparable book has been published by L. S. Tong and G. J. Weisman for PWRs.

Additional tests were performed subsequently at Dresden-1 to determine the margins available in terms of thermal performance and stability. It was found that the power level could be raised by 50 percent and remain below the latest CHF limit lines. Also, core stability tests were carried out by oscillating a control rod and measuring the decay in the produced neutron flux. The plant remained stable after increasing its void content by 50 percent. *In retrospect, meaningful tests in operating plants can best justify increases in power or power density.*

> In retrospect, meaningful tests in operating plants can best justify increases in power or power density.

The Dresden-1 audit, finally, may have contributed to the GE decision to accept AEC funding to develop the BWR in the early 1960s. There was a realization that the cost of GE alone developing the BWR might become excessive. Potential customers were interested in supporting high power density, superheat, and compact BWR demonstration plants if they could benefit from AEC participation. Also, it was apparent that Westinghouse was taking increased advantage of their involvement in the Naval Reactor Program and that GE could gain from similar arrangements.

The role of Development Engineering, which was managed by Don Imhoff, increased considerably due to AEC funding. The organization was subdivided into three groups. The first one dealt with the GE-funded development of pressure suppression containment and the compaction features of internal steam separation and subsequently jet pumps. Charlie Robbins was in charge of that group and he was able to get PG&E to let him use the large steam supply of the Moss Landing power plant in Monterey, California, for his tests. Bob Pennington was responsible for the Experimental Vallecitos Superheat Reactor being sponsored by Niagara Mohawk, AEC, and the state of New York. My role was expanded to cover BWR projects and it included the joint AEC large fuel irradiation at the Vallecitos Boiling Water Reactor. Also, I was responsible for the high power density program to be carried out at Big Rock Point in a 70-MWe reactor, capable of operating at 1200 psia and 60 kW/L. In addition, contracts were negotiated with the AEC for heat transfer development work to operate above critical heat flux and to measure pressure drop in a large contraction–expansion geometry at high pressure. This put us in the lead in many areas of two-phase flow and heat transfer and gave us the chance to exchange results and facility design characteristics with the British, French, Belgians, and Italians. Ron Scroggins of AEC arranged a tour of European test loops during which I gave my speech in French in Belgium to the great surprise of the wife of Professor Rohsenow, who acted as our guide through Europe. She never forgave me for letting her struggle with our French train baggage handlers.

GE also received a major contract from Euratom to install a process computer at the SENN BWR plant in Italy and to perform tests to attain full power without using the dual-cycle steam generator. The negotiation of that contract with SENN in Rome brought up the differences between the American and Italian ways of doing business. The Americans had prepared a draft contract and wanted to work through lunch in order to get back home as soon as possible. The Italians insisted on having their normal extended lunchtime and needed several days for management review of the draft contract. A compromise was reached which helped me develop an appreciation for the Italians' desire to enjoy life and not just work all the time.

I was spending less time doing development work and more time preparing proposals and negotiating them. That pattern reached nearly full-time duty when trying to reach agreement with Consumers Power Company for the high power density program at Big Rock Point located in the northern part of Michigan. There was a weekly shuttle of two GE lawyers (Heimann and Lomen) and myself from San Jose to the headquarters of Consumers Power Company to discuss the development program and the commercial conditions. I nearly had an ulcer problem when Jim Campbell, the president of Consumers, stated that he would stop discussing issues with a scientist and insisted upon the presence of a top GE officer who could make commercial decisions. He was right because an agreement was reached at the next meeting between officers of the two companies and I was able to reduce my milk intake back to normal.

The Big Rock Point demonstration plant had a variable-speed, forced water circulation system instead of the natural circulation design used at the twin Humboldt Bay plant located in California. It also had a dry spherical containment and a large external steam drum rather than the compact features of pressure suppression and internal natural steam separation. Its core design was modified to reduce costs by enlarging the spacing between control rods and reducing their number. (Incidentally, I had to explain to our newest vice president why we were not using a single control rod). Also, the core support location was changed to its top, as had been done in PWRs. Finally, Big Rock Point was to be the first BWR with a process computer to track plant conditions and to perform online reactor core calculations without any interference with control functions. The process computer was very helpful in re-creating prevailing conditions during unanticipated transients. The design and construction of Big Rock Point went very well. Fred Hollenback was the GE project manager and Bechtel the architect-engineer. There was no licensing intervention and the test program started on schedule but was set back when growing neutron flux oscillations were observed. Initially, the anomaly was attributed to reactor instability. I was informed of that possibility while attending the Third International Conference on the Peaceful Uses of Atomic Energy. My wife and our daughter had accompanied me on that trip and our plans included a short trip to Casablanca, Morocco, to look over my old living quarters and a few days of vacation in Switzerland to take the little train ride to Zermatt and the Matterhorn. Upon our return to the United States, John Corr, a top GE structural engineer, determined that the oscillations were due to flow-induced vibrations at the top core support location. A support redesign was implemented that required a major repair to be carried out inside the pressure vessel by trained water diving personnel. *In retrospect, many light water reactors have developed flow-induced vibrations and the ensuing repairs have been very costly. New pressure vessel internal designs need to be subjected to correctly scaled tests to avoid plant repairs.* After the Big Rock Point support was corrected, the plant achieved its goal of operating at 60 kW/L or about 50 percent higher than previously demonstrated. Those tests justified the later increase of power density in future BWRs.

Another important objective of the Big Rock Point program was to reduce fuel costs by improving the fuel assembly design and by employing stainless steel fuel cladding with different fuel fabrication processes such as swaging cladding atop fuel pellets or using vibratory compaction of powdered fuel. That part of the work produced a simplified fuel design with no tie rod or segmented fuel rods but it failed in its fabrication efforts due to stress corrosion cracking of the stainless steel cladding. *In retrospect, the implications of that early failure of stainless steel fuel cladding in oxygenated water at high stresses may not have been put to full use in later BWR failures of stainless steel piping and reactor internals.*

> In retrospect, many light water reactors have developed flow-induced vibrations and the ensuing repairs have been very costly. New pressure vessel internal designs need to be subjected to correctly scaled tests to avoid plant repairs.

There were other noteworthy accomplishments at Big Rock Point. For example, the strong GE team of nuclear physicists consisting of David Fischer, Russ Crowther, and Bob Haling conceived of and successfully implemented the use of gadolinium as a burnable poison, which was used in all subsequent BWR fuel designs. The same group introduced the first practical three-dimensional computer model of an operating BWR as well as the Haling principle for minimizing power peaking during core burnup.

There was one last hurdle to meeting the commercial commitments at Big Rock Point: the warranted plant output. I was in the control room when the plant failed to meet the required output at a pressure of 1000 psia. It was fortunate that the plant was licensed to operate at 1200 psia and steam tables could be used to determine the pressure increase needed to meet the warranty. The decision was made to raise the pressure settings carefully and one at a time with the plant operating. It was done safely and the warranty performance run was completed satisfactorily to allow test personnel to leave before Christmas. *In retrospect, such online manipulations currently would not be allowed, irrespective of Christmas, without stringent assessments and independent review by the regulatory authority in order to avoid Chernobyl-type accidents.*

> In retrospect, such online manipulations currently would not be allowed without stringent assessments and independent review by the regulatory authority in order to avoid Chernobyl-type accidents.

During my years in Development Engineering, my involvement in BWR design was rather limited. I recollect participating in a marketing presentation to the utility considering the purchase of Oyster Creek. I discussed GE expectations to raise the CHF limit and to support the ability to increase or "stretch" the Oyster Creek output by 20 percent on a best effort basis (which was satisfied readily). While "stretch" helped the sale, the principal reason for the contract was the reduced price offered by GE. It was based on selling six to eight nearly identical plants and getting the benefit of volume. Unfortunately, only one other similar plant, Nine Mile 1, was purchased and its design diverged quickly from Oyster Creek's design because its sale was on a nuclear systems basis rather than a turnkey basis, as in the case of Oyster Creek. *In retrospect, the benefit of sales volume and a learning curve was not achieved because the sales involved a long cycle of regulated product, high capital costs, and customers with their own preference for features. The chance for success may improve with the current reduced number of nuclear power plant owners. Its acceptance, however, remains doubtful as long as choices for electrical power facilities remain dominated by market and its short-cycle forces and customer preferences.*

After the "economic" Oyster Creek sale, the competition intensified and the model improvements and increases in power output accelerated. In the mid-1960s, GE engineering, under Bob Richards, was working on several BWR models at the same time. The Mark BWR-2 was assigned to Oyster Creek and its output of 500 to 600 MWe. Dresden-2 was labeled BWR-3 because of the addition of internal jet pumps and an output of about 800 MWe. The design of the Mark BWR-4 at Browns Ferry had just been initiated and it had an output of 1200 MWe and an increased power density of 45 kW/L. Bob Richards was not satisfied with the design production of all these models and asked the engineering functional group at GE Headquarters to assess his organization and to recommend improvements. The final decision from the organization study was to form a Systems Engineering subsection reporting to Bob Richards who selected me to manage it. I was quite reluctant to leave my position because I had an outstanding boss, Don Imhoff, who gave me maximum management latitude. During my six years in Development Engineering, I had published seven technical articles in recognized magazines. Also, I had been asked to present invited talks on two-phase flow at the ASME annual meeting and at the Symposium on Two-Phase Flow at the University of Exeter in England (see Figure 3.1). I was selected by the AEC to present a summary paper on critical heat flux with J. Batch of Hanford and J. Casterline of Columbia University at the Third International Conference on the Peaceful Uses of Atomic Energy. Finally, I had become chairman of the ASME Heat Transfer Division and received its Heat Transfer Memorial Award in 1966. My six years in Development Engineering were productive and may have exceeded my expectations if I had chosen to pursue an academic career. It would have been easy—but less challenging—to go on doing the same work. My main contribution had been to insist on full-scale critical heat flux tests at BWR conditions in the ATLAS loop shown in Figure 3.2 and a much better understanding of BWR core behavior, which allowed increases in reactor core power density and steam void content. I felt that I could continue to influence facility decisions in the future (which I did in the case of flow-induced vibrations and core spray tests). My final decision was to respond to the strong urging of Dr. R. B. Richards and I agreed to take on the challenge of the offered promotion even though I did not understand the reasons for my selection for a design position.

Figure 3.1.   Some of the attendees at the Symposium on Two-Phase Flow at the University of Exeter, England. Left to right: Dr. S. Levy (General Electric Corp., San Jose, California); Professor A. E. Dukler (Department of Chemical Engineering, University of Houston, Houston, Texas. U.S. Representative on the Organising Committee for the Symposium); Professor S. S. Kutateladze (Director, The Institute of Heat Physics, Novosibirsk, U.S.S.R.); Professor P. M. C. Lacey (Department of Chemical Engineering, University of Exeter. Chairman of the Organising Committee for the Symposium); Professor D. B. Spalding (Department of Mechanical Engineering, Imperial College of Science and Technology, London); Professor B. M. Smolski (Deputy Director, The Institute for Heat and Mass Transfer, Minsk, U.S.S.R.).
(Source: Symposium Proceedings, 1965)

Speaking of career evolution, I remember my fortuitous contribution to the Jack Welch role at GE. Jack Welch was a graduate student seeking his Ph.D. at the University of Illinois under Professor Jim Westwater who was visiting San Jose at that time to help with the high-pressure transparent test section being built by Frank Tippetts. Shortly thereafter, Welch's résumé reached my office and I had to tell him that we had no

Figure 3.2.   ATLAS heat transfer loop. (Courtesy of General Electric)

open position because of a reduced budget. Many years later, I had the chance to attend top GE management meetings when Welch was the company vice chairman. Jack put his arm on my shoulders and offered to buy me a free drink (they were all free) for keeping him from joining the GE nuclear business instead of the plastic business where he scored his first big success.

FOUR

THE ENGINEERING MANAGEMENT YEARS

The management years cover a period of 11 years, from 1966 to 1977. They include about one and one-half years as manager of Systems Engineering and three years as manager of Design Engineering. In 1971, I was appointed general manager of the Nuclear Fuel Department and subsequently promoted to general manager of the Boiling Water Reactor Systems Department in 1973 and eventually to general manager of Boiling Water Operations in 1975. Because the problems to be solved changed with each of the above assignments, this chapter is devoted to the engineering management years and it is subdivided into two sections: Systems Engineering and Design Engineering.

SYSTEMS ENGINEERING

The switch from development to systems engineering was a big shock. The number of issues to be resolved was rather large and there were tight schedules to be met. At the same time, licensing requirements were escalating and design changes were necessary. In addition, there was an expectation that the formation of a Systems Engineering organization would streamline and accelerate the production of information. Good managers were assigned to the newly formed group and they made significant improvements. Phil Bray was the manager of Safety

Conformance and Lee Fidrych was the manager of Systems Design. Mike Larocco handled Proposal Engineering. Phil Bray was excellent at identifying the necessary solutions and generating them on a specified schedule even when he broadened their scope to avoid having to redo the analyses. He was famous for his presentations on colored transparency charts and he often surprised his listeners by having backup charts available to answer questions. His top lieutenant was Pio Ianni who gained the full respect of the regulators by admitting that he did not have all the answers and would get them. Lee Fidrych produced system descriptions, flow diagrams, and process and instrumentation diagrams (P&IDs) to control key system characteristics. *In retrospect, this system approach reduced the work required to deal with different plant output and different plant models. The format of the P&IDs was very useful later for training operators and for generating operating procedures. Later on, those documents were expanded to cover safety needs, such as startup times as well as emergency power requirements.* Another key part of the organization was run by Mike Larocco and supported the needs of marketing. His group was responsible for the flow rate of water in the boiler and its heat balance. It also developed a suspended three-dimensional drawing of the boiler around which architect-engineers (AEs) could wrap the containment.

The first major escalation GE faced at that time was the licensing decision to deal mechanistically with a loss-of-coolant accident (LOCA). GE had reluctantly agreed with the regulatory authorities to design boiling water reactors (BWRs) for the instantaneous double-ended break of the largest pipe attached to the reactor pressure vessel. The requirements were being escalated to design for the jet forces leaving the broken pipe as well as the resulting pipe whip. GE resisted that demand because it did not believe in instantaneous large breaks and because it would require the installation of large piping restraints within the containment drywell, making it much more difficult to carry out normal maintenance in already crowded areas. GE finally agreed to the change to avoid a considerable delay in the issuance of construction permits for plants under review.

Another important issue was the adequacy of the emergency cooling systems and their ability to keep the fuel cool during a LOCA. *The loss-of-coolant accident took on a new perspective when it was realized that complete failure of cooling could lead to a core meltdown,* which, under extremely improbable conditions, would leave the reactor vessel and penetrate the containment concrete basemat to produce what became known as the famous China Syndrome. That was an unfortunate misnomer because any hypothetical meltdown

The loss-of-coolant accident took on a new perspective when it was realized that complete failure of cooling could lead to a core meltdown,

would arrest itself as it grew. Also, its initiator was highly improbable because it presumed an instantaneous break of the largest available pipe combined with an earthquake, a single failure, and the loss of normal power. It was then called the *worst credible accident,* and justifiably so.

On October 27, 1966, the director of government regulation, Harold Price, appointed a "task force to conduct a review of power reactor emergency core cooling systems and core protection." The task force was to examine how to augment the cooling systems to prevent substantial core meltdown and how to cope with large molten masses of fuel. The task force had representatives from the national laboratories, industry, and representatives from the AEC, as shown in Figure 4.1. This was likely the first and probably the last time that members from regulatory agencies, national laboratories, and industry were brought together to resolve a problem in spite of concerns about conflict of interest. That conflict-of-interest rule can prevent balanced and reasonable suggestions from being developed in some cases.

The task force report recommended additional steps to improve the integrity of the primary system. It also pointed out that a leak would develop before a large break and that a leak detection system should be installed to stop its propagation. *In retrospect, the leak-before-break assumption took another 30 years to be accepted and to remove some of the large piping restraints installed in the 1960s.*

The report also pointed out that uncertainties in large-break behavior unnecessarily complicated the design of emergency cooling systems and decreased their reliability. The report also recommended additional core

EMERGENCY CORE COOLING

REPORT OF ADVISORY TASK FORCE ON POWER
REACTOR EMERGENCY COOLING

W. K. Ergen, Chairman

Louis Baker, Jr.

E. S. Beckjord

A. P. Bray

Joseph Dietrich

Salomon Levy

I. H. Mandil

D. L. Morrison

W. E. Nyer

J. M. Waage

R. E. Wascher

T. R. Wilson

In addition, J. J. DiNunno of the Commission's Regulatory Staff and
J. A. Lieberman of the AEC's Division of Reactor Development and Technology participated in the deliberations of the Task Force. R. J. Impara
of the Commission's Regulatory Staff served as Technical Secretary.

Figure 4.1.   Representatives of the Advisory Task Force on Power Reactor
Emergency Cooling. (Source: U.S. Atomic Energy Report, 1967)

cooling tests at higher temperatures and with degraded geometry. With respect to large molten masses, the poor state of knowledge was highlighted as well as the inability to define the size, composition, temperature, release configurations, formation times, and means to cope with them. Preliminary evaluations regarding cooling the bottom of the pressure vessel and the use of core catchers or crucibles were made but their benefit was not quantifiable. *In retrospect, too much time was spent dealing with hypothetical conditions that could have been better applied to the reliability of safety systems to inhibit the hypothetical conditions from occurring.*

> In retrospect, too much time was spent dealing with hypothetical conditions that could have been better applied to the reliability of safety systems to inhibit the hypothetical conditions from occurring.

The Report of the Advisory Task Force on Power Reactor Emergency Cooling led to the requirement that all nuclear power plants must have emergency core cooling (ECC) systems. (Interestingly, the GE Safety Council had imposed that same rule on BWRs several years earlier.) The report was a shock to many who believed that the containment was a last ditch barrier capable of handling any arbitrary failure of the two preceding barriers—fuel cladding and primary system envelope. The immediate result was insistence on more protection. It led to the addition of an accumulator on PWRs to cover the entire break spectrum and to the installation of a flooding system on BWRs because of concerns about the core spray system flow distribution. The changes were costly because they were made to plants undergoing detailed design and construction. The impact, however, was much more lasting. *In retrospect, the emphasis on large breaks and their complexity reduced the attention being given to the more frequent small breaks and operator errors, which later produced the Three Mile Island (TMI) accident.* In the BWR case, Bray jokingly used to point out that there were so many cooling systems that they might float the reactor vessel. In a paper presented at a conference at the IAEA in 1967, I tried to diffuse the concern about large molten masses and pleaded for a systems approach to containment design (Levy, S., "Containment and Siting of Nuclear Power Plants," International

Atomic Energy Agency, Vienna, 1967). The approach recognized that containment is only part of a total system preventing and limiting the consequences of a release of fission products. The containment performance requirements would be determined by looking at the overall system rather than by making arbitrary assumptions about the source of the accident and the effectiveness of some of the provided features. *In retrospect, many years later, arbitrary and inconsistent assumptions are still being employed in safety analyses.*

Once the realization set in that containment was not an absolute barrier, the licensing approval process became much more difficult. At that time, GE was seeking approval for their BWR-4 model represented by the Tennessee Valley Authority (TVA) Browns Ferry units. The increased output of that design and, in particular, its increased specific power came under considerable scrutiny from the Advisory Committee on Reactor Safeguards (ACRS) and especially from Dr. Dave Okrent from UCLA. I attended every meeting because approval of that model was so important to GE. A lot of preparations were made for each trip to Washington. Charts were drafted to respond to topics identified by ACRS. They were rehearsed and modified to fit management comments. Agreement was reached on backup charts. Another rehearsal was held with the customer the night before the meeting. My participation was limited to make sure that our answers were correct and responsive to the questions asked. I still remember one case of direct involvement when the strength of highly oxidized Zircaloy was being discussed. GE had brought a piece of fully oxidized Zircaloy-clad tubing to pass around. When I applied pressure to its ends, it failed easily and my spontaneous reaction was to say that it surely was brittle. I passed the two broken pieces to the ACRS members while I sat down quietly. The customer did not think very much of that demonstration. That event, however, may have contributed to the chairman of ACRS stating to a top Commonwealth Edison licensing representative that it was a real pleasure to do business with Levy.

Every time we left San Jose, we were in a high mood because it was supposed to be our last meeting, but there were many disappointing return flights. *In retrospect, over the years, one realizes that regulators have the upper hand and seldom lose.* The Browns Ferry hold-up was settled finally by recognizing that specific power was a generic issue applicable to all reactors and a generic report needed to be submitted to support the proposed design. *That strategy led to an epidemic number of generic topics to be tracked and resolved over long periods of time. From 1983 to 2003, the program processed approximately 840 generic issues and it has grown well beyond its original purpose of dealing with essential and generic safety issues.*

In addition to the difficulties on the licensing front, GE had to reconsider the scope of its nuclear offering. Most GE contracts were for turnkey projects and they were turning out to be less and less profitable. The primary reason was that the GE contracts did not provide enough for the increases in field costs. Experienced AEs required that fieldwork be on a time and materials basis while GE did not. Another secondary reason was that GE had to assume responsibility for some licensing changes. The resolution favored by GE Marketing was to adopt a nuclear system scope with much reduced fieldwork and a sharing arrangement for the licensing risks. *GE Engineering had a strong preference for turnkey because it increased the chances for plant design standardization and gave the engineers much stronger control of their interfaces with the architect-engineers.* Engineering pointed out that the nuclear scope would vary with the plant sale and the AE assigned to it. At that time GE was working with Bechtel, Burns and Roe, Ebasco, Sargent and Lundy, Stone and Webster, and TVA, which acted as its own AE. After considerable debate, the end result was predictable and a nuclear systems scope was adopted, but continued tension prevailed between GE Marketing and Engineering.

To overcome the impact of that decision, the description of the GE nuclear systems at the proposal stage was enlarged to increase the chance of being paid for design changes produced by others. Also, GE developed a large set of balance-of-plant requirements to be followed by the AEs. That document was not well received and many AEs penalized GE for such requirements. In particular, it was reported that the low chloride concentration demanded after a condenser tube leak could not be satisfied. *In retrospect, much tighter coolant chemistry conditions have been required in subsequent years to protect the BWR pressure vessel internals*

In retrospect, much tighter coolant chemistry conditions have been required in subsequent years to protect the BWR pressure vessel internals and the PWR steam generators.

and the PWR steam generators. Materials performance is another key topic that never received the long-term attention it deserved.

GE faced its first major problem in both areas when cracks were found on stub tubes attached to the bottom of the Oyster Creek pressure vessel. A leak was detected at that location during the ASME (American Society of Mechanical Engineers) Code approval test. A panel of experts assembled by the manager of engineering confirmed that it was caused by stress corrosion cracking because the water used was not purified and may have contained such contaminants as chloride. The stub tube stainless steel was sensitized when the stubs and the carbon steel pressure vessel were annealed in a furnace. Also, the stresses are at their highest value during the overpressure test. The resolution consisted of removing all stub tube cracks and covering susceptible areas with a 308L weld overlay, which is much more resistant to stress corrosion cracking. This was a very difficult and costly repair that had a significant impact on the Oyster Creek startup schedule.

Typical of such declining performance, the remedy at GE was often a change in organization. A new vice president, Gene Schubert, was assigned to run the business and the manager of marketing, George Stathakis, was promoted to general manager of the Atomic Power Equipment Department (APED). George was a graduate of Berkeley where he received his M.S. degree in 1953 from Professor Drake. He was the only engineer playing as a lineman on the football team, and he played quite well. The rearrangement did not help ease the tension between George and my boss, Bob Richards. As the Oyster Creek situation continued to deteriorate, the decision was made to split the engineering function into two organizations: a Development Group under Don Imhoff and a Design Engineering Section under me. Bob Richards was asked to take over the Engineering Section of a newly formed Fuel Department. In the meantime, the repair at Oyster Creek had deteriorated to include sensitized stainless steel rings attached to the pressure vessel nozzles to eliminate dissimilar metal welding in the field, and they required the same repair as the stub tubes.

My assignment in Systems Engineering had lasted about 18 months. During that time, I had good exposure to the customers and the nuclear regulatory process. Also, I started to become familiar with two critical problem areas: emergency core cooling and stainless stress corrosion failure. Those issues were to reappear several times during my career.

DESIGN ENGINEERING

In the new organizational scheme, Phil Bray took over Systems Engineering. Jens Kjemtrup became the manager of Proposal Engineering. Lee Fidrych was in charge of Plant and Equipment Engineering. Tom Trocki was the manager of Component Engineering ,and Dave Long was in charge of Engineering Production and Control. With Bray in charge of the topic of emergency core cooling, I was able to concentrate on the stress corrosion cracking of sensitized stainless steel and to pursue ways to reduce our increasing backlog of documents.

The Oyster Creek problem appeared again in the first Tarapur pressure vessel and its dual-cycle steam generator, which were being built in India. After listening to Expert Panel findings, I went to Tarapur to explain our corrective action plan because there was limited disagreement about removing the vessel cladding if it was cracked. During the trip from the Bombay airport to the GE apartment, I was shocked by the number of families occupying the middle strip on the highway to and from the airport. The families had decided to reside on that middle strip to benefit from the electrical lighting provided along the highway. The following day, I took the train to the site where several children were waiting to beg for money from the passengers. During my stay in India, I seldom saw many children smile because they were too preoccupied with getting work or food rather than playing with each other. There was a stark contrast between the site and the poor Bombay quarters I had visited. An entire new village had been constructed, including dormitories, cafeterias, and homes for the managers. Even a large outdoor movie facility was available. The facilities were all to be turned over to the plant operators and supporting staff at the end of the project.

I was given a tour of the power plants and it was clear that they were approaching the end of construction. I crawled through a cut circulation pipe to reach the bottom of the vessel and to observe the removal of cracks. An accelerated welding training course was being implemented to carry out the repair on a three-shift basis. The emphasis was on quality assurance and multiple inspections. A militaristic approach was utilized, and the native welders readily accepted it because it gave them an opportunity to join a trade they had been excluded from in the past.

Discussions were held at the site about the proposed repair and I was asked to extend my visit in India until the weekend when I could meet with the chairman of the India Atomic Energy Commission. Hubbard, a GE materials engineer, was a great help in the Tarapur meetings and made me aware that the GE design engineers could specify their choice of material without review or approval by materials specialists. (Hubbard was asked to initiate a materials handbook upon his return to San Jose and a formal approval for materials became necessary before proceeding with equipment purchases.)

I had the chance to visit with project and engineering personnel and their families and found that the conversation always strayed to stomach and digestion problems and the different pills that were taken to overcome them. Some of the wives were grateful for the cooking and cleaning help they received, while others missed their family and friends at home and wished they could go back. Interestingly, the complainers, upon their return, were the most enthusiastic about their international experience. Most engineers tended to be indifferent as long as the work was challenging. During my last day at the site, I tried to look at a defect found on the index tube of a control rod drive. A guard with a drawn bayonet stopped me from entering until I was cleared by the project. I was told that the increased security had nothing to do with my suspicious looks but with the disappearance of parts and especially copper from the plant.

Friday was spent riding the train back to Bombay, visiting an old British private club with new and proud Indian Tarapur management members, and preparing a summary presentation for the chairman of the

India Atomic Energy Commission (IAEC). On early Saturday, I visited the Hanging Gardens of Bombay where I was struck by the density of persons trying to enjoy that beautiful park.

The meeting with the IAEC chairman went well. The root cause of the problem and the proposed repair were explained. With respect to removing cracks found on the pressure vessel cladding, the argument was made that, without their removal, the cracks would grow faster and reach the base metal sooner. The argument for not removing them was that their growth through the base metal would not be influenced by their progress through the cladding. The discussion never became contentious because there were no data for crack growth in bimetallic structures.

I rushed from the meeting to catch the last Air India plane with stops in Cairo, Athens, and Frankfurt with a connection to New York and eventually San Francisco. On the flight back, I worried about the prevailing class system in India because it made it very difficult to progress especially with a rapidly growing population. I did not dwell too long on that insurmountable problem, and was soon looking forward to getting back to California.

I have not had the chance to go back to Tarapur or India since 1968, but I still remember it as a beautiful site located on the Indian Ocean where nuclear plants were expected to generate badly needed electricity to eliminate the nearly daily loss of overloaded fossil power plants and to improve the standard of living of a growing population in that region of India.

Back in the United States, the Oyster Creek repair received intensive reviews and observations by the regulators. After several meetings, the repair was approved by the ACRS at a meeting I attended with new GE Project General Manager R. L. Dickeman. Design Engineering's recommendation was to apply the same fix to all pressure vessels with sensitized stainless steel. Because the proposed change would result in significant plant schedule delays, the project group passed the engineering position to the customers but left the final decision up to them. Most plants implemented the retrofit except for one turnkey plant which convinced itself that its material was of superior grade and one nuclear steam supply plant which was found to have no cracks on stub tubes after the ASME vessel overpressure test. The latter customer wanted an estimate of the time for cracks to initiate and grow. I signed off on the estimate after using a draft prepared by GE materials engineers who included appropriate uncertainties. By that time, many corrosion loops were operating with coupons at different stress levels and using excess oxygen concentrations to accelerate the time to failure. Preliminary results were showing that sensitization of stainless steel would reduce its lifetime by about a factor of 2. At the request of that same utility, a study was completed to show that, after startup, a repair of the stub tubes would be extremely difficult but possible.

After the trip to India, the primary focus shifted to scheduling and producing documents for BWR projects. There was no definite and agreed-on list of required documents nor a specific schedule for their issuance. It took several iterations among Design Engineering and the project managers to produce a preliminary document list and a tentative schedule. Each document now had the name of an engineer responsible for its generation and schedule. When a schedule date was missed or changed, the original promised date was left on the schedule to detect multiple delays or long schedule slippage. The project managers had been given full access to the engineers performing their work, but such access had in the past led to changes in schedules without determining their impact on the entire workload. A requisition-engineering function was created and it became responsible for all changes to the committed engineering dates.

Engineers are expected to solve problems but they tend to be creative and make changes to designs. To hold down the number of changes, a plant design freeze was implemented when the design had progressed to a certain point. Beyond that point, changes were subjected to review by a multifunctional team headed by the manager of Requisition Engineering. I participated in some meetings to establish standards for accepting changes. Many good ideas were saved for future BWR models. At the same time, many engineers became aware of the delay and high costs associated with getting approval from the customer, regulators, AEs, and equipment vendors.

Finally, an acceptable target was needed for the backlog, that is, the number of documents remaining to be generated to satisfy our schedule commitments. That target was established by assuming limited productivity gains. The goal was advertised throughout the engineering building and reported weekly. If the target was reached, the promise was made to take every employee to dinner and the offer included secretaries, drafting personnel, and engineering assistants. When the first decrease in backlog was achieved, an entirely different attitude developed. A teamwork atmosphere prevailed with the employees helping each other without prodding by management. There was a slight setback when the vice president decided to record the late arrival of a few engineers to work. (Other nonprofessional employees were required to punch time cards.) I started to tour the building after the closing hour and I encouraged the noticeable number of engineers working late to record their departure time. When that strategy failed to be recognized, I started to arrive early every morning and stayed in my car until I could sign in late. That support of the engineers, which was visible to the late arrivals as they walked by my car, led to abandonment of late signup sheets. *In retrospect, definitive schedules, a design freeze, multifunctional reviews of changes, teamwork, and ownership by engineers and management eventually helped meet GE commitments in spite of the leadership of a development engineer!*

After a lot of hard teamwork, the target was reached and the dinner date was set. I came close to missing the meal because of bad weather in Cincinnati where I was participating in the closing of a BWR sale with George Stathakis. I made it while the main dish was being served. Phil Bray acted as the master of ceremony and his Irish ancestry helped make it a very enjoyable evening. The vice president attended and expressed his appreciation to an audience becoming more and more raucous as the evening progressed.

The Oyster Creek plant was purchased in 1963. Between 1965 and 1967, 50 new nuclear plants were ordered. The competition for sales was intensifying with Combustion Engineering (CE) and Babcock & Wilcox (B&W) entering the market. Most proposal evaluations were now being carried out by AEs and they emphasized total plant costs with insufficient attention being given to plant reliability.

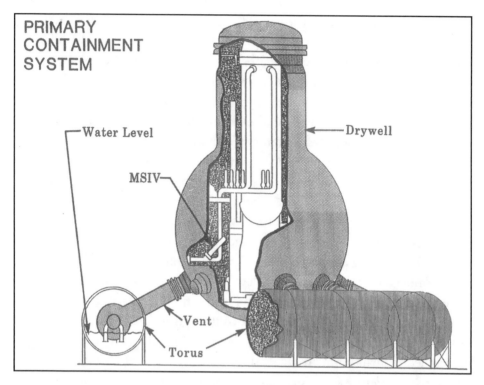

Figure 4.2.   Mark I containment design. (Courtesy of General Electric)

All the early GE sales had used the Mark I containment shown in Figure 4.2. That design consisted of an inverted light bulb–shaped drywell and a donut-shaped pressure suppression torus. If a pipe break occurred inside the drywell, the air/water/steam mixture would rush through vent pipes into the wetwell, and the water inside the torus would quench the steam, reducing the pressure and minimizing the possibility of any leakage into the reactor building.

That configuration was judged to be costly and difficult to construct by some AEs, so GE had to introduce a new Mark II prismatic containment arrangement chopped at the top. This over-under concept employed a water wetwell at the bottom with vertical vent pipes connecting it to a drywell located above. That Mark II containment allowed the use of a concrete structure with a steel liner. It was adopted even though it required redoing all the boiler piping drawings within the drywell. That

BWR design was labeled BWR-5. It followed the BWR-4 model assigned to the Browns Ferry class of reactors. *In retrospect, GE had coupled its BWR offering to the pressure suppression containment concept and GE was forced to compensate for increases in containment cost evaluations even though the containment was under the scope of the AEs.* This anomaly confirmed Dr. Richards' concern about a nuclear systems scope but it could be tolerated as long as the market kept

Instability in the backlog of plant orders added to production difficulties and increasing capital costs.

growing to reach a banner year of 38 plants ordered in 1973.

At the end of 1973, there was an oil embargo and the subsequent increase in oil prices produced an economic recession. Many of the plants were delayed and canceled in later years due to reduced electricity demand, construction delays, increased costs, opposition to nuclear power, and licensing changes. *That instability in the backlog of plant orders added to production difficulties and increasing capital costs.*

GE had selected pressure suppression containment because the volume and design pressure were reduced compared to that in a dry containment. It also had the advantage of providing a large protected water pool for emergency core cooling and scrubbing of fission products released during accidents. Pacific Gas & Electric (PG&E) was the first to recognize those advantages and helped Charley Robbins of GE develop and introduce it at the Humboldt Bay power plant in California. Its next application was to be at Bodega Bay but that plant was abandoned due to opposition to nuclear power and concerns about earthquakes. The regulators tended to prefer dry containment because it was easier to analyze, but they tried to remain neutral on the choice of containment. *In retrospect, the benefits of pressure suppression were never reflected in the licensing process and total plant costs,* which left GE primarily responsible for its performance and costs. Interestingly, Westinghouse, the nuclear power plant market share leader, must have discovered some merit to pressure suppression because, in the early 1970s, they introduced a containment system that used ice instead of water for the same function.

Two other changes were made in the BWR-5 model. Continued

studies of emergency core cooling showed that a full pressure core spray system with its own diesel generator would simplify the BWR network and that modification was well received. The other change was pushed by the Marketing Department and it was to control the reactor flow with a valve instead of motor generator sets, which were more costly and used electrical power. *In retrospect, the choice of a control valve over motor generator sets to control flow was not wise because it sacrificed plant operability for a minimal decrease in costs.*

In retrospect, the choice of a control valve over motor generator sets to control flow was not wise because it sacrificed plant operability for a minimal decrease in costs.

To my great surprise, I found that I could enjoy production work. There was much less room to be creative but I faced sufficient challenges such as resolving how to get 630 persons to work together as an efficient team, how to respond to competitive thrusts, and how to maneuver through regulatory and antinuclear minefields. Good communication was the key to achieving teamwork and it involved definition of goals, progress reports against goals, staff meetings, managing by walking, timely performance reviews, and an open-door policy. Engineers were involved in decisions by asking them to consider various alternatives and come up with a recommendation. *The strategy was to err on the side of safety and not bury problems; rather they were encouraged to present them for resolution because they would surface eventually and then cost that much more to be resolved.*

The biggest problem was low completion of plant design and equipment specifications at the time of sale. The large number of plant models and power outputs did not help. *Coupled with poorly defined and evolving regulations, it is not surprising that plant costs increased and schedules were stretched.* In retrospect, reaching agreement at the interfaces was always a challenge because the parties involved were protecting their own interests. For example, the nuclear systems suppliers worked on reducing the stresses in their piping while the architect-engineers tried to decrease loads on their supports. *Another difficult obstacle was the rising activist voice against nuclear power and its safety.*

In 1970, I had two opportunities to get involved in antinuclear matters. In the first case I was asked to attend congressional hearings on radioactive effluents from nuclear power plants with GE Vice President Gene Schubert. The critics were recommending that radioactive releases be reduced because the number of nuclear plants and their power output were growing. It was pointed out that the incremental radiation dose to any actual person inside

Another difficult obstacle was the rising activist voice against nuclear power and its safety.

or outside the plant was being controlled irrespective of the number of operating plants and their output. It was reiterated that nuclear power plants were being designed and operated to minimize both volume and radioactivity of effluents wherever practical. The radiation doses to the workers and general public had to be kept at a small fraction of the permissible values and of the recommendations of the International Commission for Radiological Protection. Finally, an augmented charcoal system was described to provide an activity reduction factor of about 100 outside the plant by an off-gas BWR system where such reduction was justified.

Shortly thereafter, the AEC published amendments to its 10 CFR Part 20 and 10 CFR Part 50 regulations which required keeping nuclear plant effluents at an *as low as practicable level.* The GE position with respect to the proposed amendments to Parts 20 and 50 was published in a paper (which I co-authored with C. E. Kent and J. Smith) at the Symposium on Environmental Aspects of Nuclear Power Stations organized by the International Atomic Energy Agency (IAEA) in 1970. One of the paper's conclusions was that "a proper design objective is a dose of the order of 5 millirems per year to any actual neighbor, which would satisfy the objective of as low as practicable." During this discussion, Westinghouse announced that their PWRs had zero radioactive release. That surprising position of zero release added confusion to the process because it is impossible to have no radioactive leakage and no low waste shipments from nuclear sites.

That first involvement with the antinuclear movement convinced me that only the critics gained from it. They gained credibility because the regulations were changed to as low as practical without quantifying how to apply that rule. (That term was modified later to *as low as reasonably achievable, ALARA). In retrospect, the strategy should have been to emphasize the poor understanding of radiation by the critics due to their failure to employ a person rather than a population dose rate. Also, industry should have stressed how the dose rate in operating plants was well below the permissible limits and was being reduced where reasonable.*

My second experience happened in May 1970 when I was asked to participate in a panel of five experts to respond to the cover page of *Power Engineering* on the subject of "NUCLEAR SAFETY: The critics cry, the doubters shout, the ill-informed flail away" (see Figure 4.3). The other panel members were P. Tomkins, Executive Director, Federal Radiation Council (FRC); Dr. C. K. Beck, Deputy Director of Regulations, AEC; D. McElroy, Vice President, Engineering, Northern States Power; and W. Carbiener, Project Director, Nuclear Reactor Accident Analytical Project, Battelle Memorial Institute. Tomkins explained the advisory role of the FRC to the president of the United States. Their recommendations were expressed in terms of exposure to people, not in terms of how the exposure got there. Dr. Beck pointed out that 13 power reactors were operating, 21 more were under review for an operating license, 26 others had construction permits, and 23 further reactors were applying for construction.

While Cliff Beck was convinced that the commission "had a very definite, unique, philosophic approach to safety and a conceptual plan for achieving safety," he also noted that the licensing process was lengthening due to increased depth of review, lack of standardization, and a rapidly developing technology. He was looking to the development of standards and codes by industry and the application of quality assurance to cope with the large licensing load.

Dave McElroy highlighted the difficulties of gaining acceptance of nuclear installations in the locations where they were being built, their high capital costs, and the high cost of money. He also was concerned about obtaining qualified young people to design and operate nuclear power systems as the systems became more complex.

D. Carbiener noted that safety had certainly been the overriding consideration from the beginning of the nuclear industry and that we

Figure 4.3. May 1970 *Power Engineering* cover. (Source: *Power Engineering,* 1970)

still had gaps in knowledge that required investigation. He also discussed the severe communications problems that existed between the general public and the nuclear industry and advocated an aggressive, well-coordinated program for telling the positive side of the nuclear story.

In my comments, I pointed out that at least half of our engineering work is involved with safety and that we needed clear, specific, and stable licensing ground rules. I favored the use of an entire spectrum of accidents with prescribed consequences to get more balance in our safety assessments. Finally, I encouraged development of probabilistic and cost/benefit tools to reduce the arbitrariness of the current process and mentioned that it was impossible to have no radioactive releases.

> In retrospect, the nuclear industry has tended to be on the defensive when criticized.

These were all very good comments—which were pertinent many years later—but I did not believe that they would convince the ill-informed, the doubters, and the critics because of our direct involvement with nuclear power. *In retrospect, the nuclear industry has tended to be on the defensive when criticized. On defense, one can only limit the damage. What was needed was good offense supported by well-known outsiders and politicians to move the public. The environmental benefits of nuclear power and how it would reduce our dependence on foreign sources of energy was seldom mentioned. Unfortunately, that necessary condition existed only for a short time after the JAEC was formed and the Atoms for Peace Program was initiated.*

As the manager of the Design Engineering group, I was asked by Marketing to support selective domestic and foreign sales of BWRs. One of my most memorable visits was a trip to Israel when Egypt and Israel were both interested in buying nuclear power plants. At the final exit checkpoint from the Tel Aviv airport, I was asked to move to a different line from the rest of the passengers. The GE personnel meeting me were very troubled by my special treatment and tried to find out the reason for it. After a long debate in Hebrew, which I no longer spoke or understood, the issue turned out to be that my passport listed Jerusalem as my place of birth and the authorities believed that I had avoided the draft to serve in the Israeli armed forces. I was returned to the normal processing line after I explained that I had left the country, when it was called Palestine, at the age of four with my parents, and would not have been of much use to the Israeli army.

The following day we drove to Haifa to meet with the power company. On the way, we stopped at the projected site where the plan was to excavate a large hole in a mountain to house the power plant. After the presentation of the BWR design, there were many questions but most were related to the ability of the plant to handle very high loads and shocks, more likely related to bombs rather than seismic requirements. The power company personnel were very friendly and offered to provide a driver and a car when I mentioned my intention to visit the Jerusalem cemetery where my parents were buried.

While in Israel, I also gave a nuclear power lecture at the Technion Institute which was well attended and which went well into overtime due to the numerous questions asked. The following day, my driver showed up. He was born in India but he left and changed his name to Cohen, the other famous Jewish family name besides Levy. He was an excellent guide and gave me an outstanding tour of Jerusalem. On my flight home, I noted that the GE marketing organization was smart enough to not send me to Egypt.

My involvement with BWR fuel was small while managing Design Engineering. I was aware that our plant fuel performance was deteriorating and I suspected manufacturing problems when I was asked whether the regulators would accept the presence of a few misplaced pellets of increased enrichment in fuel rods. My reply was that I seriously doubted it without a full assessment of the safety implications. GE top management at headquarters had already initiated an independent review by a team headed by Dr. Roy Beaton. The report was quite critical and forecasted significant warranty payments unless conditions were corrected.

The immediate impact was a new organization with George Stathakis being appointed vice president of the Nuclear Energy Division. John Selby, previously the general manager of GE's Aerospace Electronic Systems Department, became the deputy division manager and was expected to support the full range of nuclear business activities. I was asked to take over the Nuclear Fuel Department and I accepted the promotion to general manager.

Before leaving the engineering production aspects of the business, I wish to recognize the accomplishments of all those I had a chance to work with. In spite of a rush of plant orders, minimal standardization of the power plants, a large number of models and plant outputs, and changing regulatory requirements, numerous BWRs were designed, licensed, constructed, operated, and reached warranted outputs. Practically, all of those BWR plants are operating safely and reliably today. Credit for those results belongs to the engineers, drafting personnel, secretaries, and engineering assistants who were responsible for that production work.

FIVE

THE GENERAL MANAGEMENT YEARS

NUCLEAR FUEL DEPARTMENT

Becoming general manager of the Nuclear Fuel Department was my first chance to run all aspects of a product business, including engineering, manufacture, marketing, project management, and profit and loss. The scope consisted of the BWR fuel assembly, its channel, and the completion of construction of a demonstration reprocessing plant located at Morris, Illinois. The fuel assembly consists of a fuel bundle and a fuel channel that surrounds it (see Figure 5.1). The fuel assembly weight is transmitted to the vessel bottom through the fuel support piece, the control rod guide tube, and the control rod housing. A fuel bundle had several fuel rods and a small number of water rods. The rods are supported by upper and lower tie plates and several spacers. The fuel channel is a 0.100-inch-thick Zircaloy-4 sheet surrounding the fuel bundle and holding the coolant flow over the entire length of the fuel assembly.

I was given a finance adviser to track performance against budget and a legal adviser for review of contracts. The two advisers came with the position of general manager but they also reported to independent functional organizations located at headquarters. I was aware that I had not been chosen to run the Nuclear Fuel Department for my business acumen but for my perceived ability to solve technical issues. My first actions were to initiate independent reviews of the fuel manufacture and its quality assurance by the functional groups at GE headquarters. The misplaced fuel pellets problem mentioned in Chapter 4 had been solved by gamma scanning the completed fuel rods and not allowing a step jump in the scan plot. That technique could be applied to fuel shipped to plant sites if returned to the factory.

Two types of fuel failure were occurring at the power plants: early life failures shortly after start of irradiation, and longer term failures after at least one fuel recycle in the reactor core. I asked Dr. Harold Klepfer to return to San Jose from Wilmington, North Carolina, to head the fuel development group. Harold was able to hire Dr. Dick Proebstle, one of the best available fuel and materials specialists, to help him.

The cause of the early failures was due to inadequate gas evacuation of some fuel rods, which allowed moisture to be present and cause the Zircaloy fuel cladding to fail as a result of internal hydriding. That problem was solved by doubling the evacuation process and by adding a moisture getter at the top of the fuel rods. That "belt and suspenders" approach eliminated hydride failures permanently. In the case of operating fuel fabricated prior to that change, the remedy consisted of locating potential failure locations by manipulating control rods and inserting control blades to reduce local power and failure growth as well as the release of fission products. In all cases, the release of fission products was kept well below values prescribed by regulators. At the end of the fuel cycle, the failed fuel assemblies were confirmed by sipping. The damaged fuel rods could be removed and replaced by replacement rods, subject to approval by the customer.

The root cause for the longer term failures was not known. Plant experience tended to show that the failure mechanisms favored increased specific power, rapid increases of power output, presence of fuel chips, and movement of control blades. The decisions was made to communicate with GE fuel owners rather than let the problem fester.

A standardized speech was written to describe our state of knowledge and it was to be presented simultaneously at three locations by

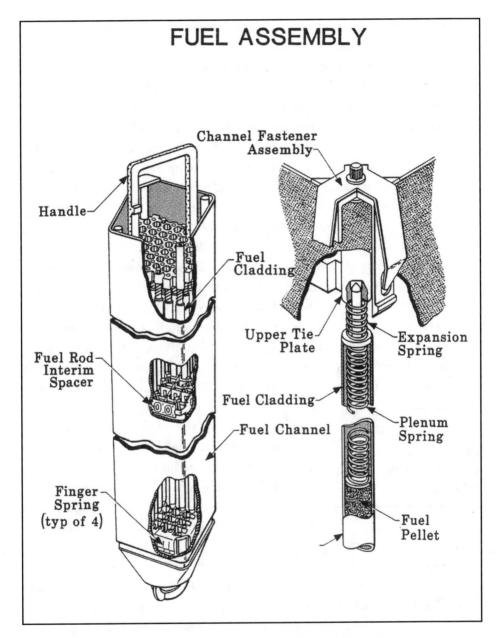

Figure 5.1.   BWR fuel assembly. (Courtesy of General Electric)

Dr. Klepfer, Tom Trocki, who was responsible for fuel design and project management, and myself. The prepared speech would commit to bringing back to the factory about 2000 fuel assemblies in order to eliminate misplaced pellets and the presence of moisture. In addition, management operating recommendations were to be implemented to slow down power changes and to reduce pellet/cladding interactions.

The basic idea was to reach the final temperature distribution within the fuel rod at full power with minimum temperature distortions as the power was increased. The recommendations consisted of using power steps and giving them a chance to stabilize before the next power step. The biggest proposed change was to modify the fuel design from 7×7 to 8×8 fuel rods to reduce the fuel specific power.

Our strategy of communication was received very well by all customers. It had the advantage of telling the customers about our problems right away and stating that we did not know the root cause for the failures. (The president of Commonwealth Edison said that it was the first time that GE had stated that they did not know the reason for a problem.) Several questions were raised about the Pellet Clad Interaction Operating Management Recommendations (PCIOMR) and their impact on plant capacity factor. It was pointed out that the fuel vendor and the plant owner had the common objective of reducing fuel failures to minimize off-gas releases and to reduce radioactivity buildup within the reactor vessel. While GE would gain from less warranty payments, the plant owner benefits would be greater because they would not incur the costs of replacing the uranium and its enrichment. *Full and open discussions with customers had paid off.*

Full and open discussions with customers had paid off.

Now back at the ranch, it was a matter of implementing the program. The independent reviews of the fuel manufacturing process and quality assurance arrived and they led to the replacement of the manager of manufacturing. According to the review, *in a large-volume manufacturing process, one should measure and control the critical parameters of the process within specified limits rather than rely on QA of the final product to catch deviations.* Manufacturing Engineering was asked to implement such a program with the help of headquarters consultants.

For quality assurance, the person in charge of the audit was hired to become the manager of quality assurance and to correct all the problems found. He was given direct access to the general manager. Engineering was to produce the new 8 × 8 fuel design on an accelerated schedule and to prepare a preliminary set of operating recommendations. Monthly management meetings were held to determine progress, to resolve differences of opinion, and to improve the relationship between Engineering and Manufacture. Drs. Klepfer and Proebstle were asked to find the root cause of the pellet/cladding interaction failures and to get maximum assistance from the GE Research Laboratory. Monthly reports were prepared for top GE management, and Dr. Roy Beaton visited San Jose to get verbal progress reports. Because the fuel warranty risks were judged to be high, the GE annual report had a summary statement mentioning the potential problem and the efforts to resolve it. The decision was made to keep the president of GE, Reg Jones, informed every three months and I had the pleasure of personally presenting that information to the president. It was obvious that Reg Jones was well briefed and I was surprised by how well he understood the issues in spite of his primary financial background.

There were several startup problems. The operating plants complained that the operating recommendations were complex and difficult to apply. GE nuclear engineers were sent to the various sites to demonstrate and explain the use of the recommendations. That experience also led to subsequent improvements in the recommendations. The fuel QA organization was swamped by customer QA personnel and their demands for information. A special group was formed to schedule and welcome the visitors as well as to encourage joint or industry type visits. The number of GE QA personnel was increased substantially and that action, along with the new fuel reliability goal of 99.98 percent, was advertised, as shown in Figure 5.2.

However, resolution of the Engineering and Manufacturing differences regarding the new design was taking too long. Those issues were discussed at length at the management meetings and the resolution was agreed to by the involved managers and the general manager. For example,

Figure 5.2.   Ad for GE's fuel reliability goal. (Source: General Electric)

the number of fuel enrichments was considered too large for fabrication purposes but not large enough to reduce the peak specific power. The decision was to have Nuclear Engineering establish a minimum number of fuel rod enrichments and to use those standard enrichments for all reloads. That compromise satisfied the needs of both Engineering and Manufacturing. Several customers voiced concern about the time needed to obtain regulatory approval for the new fuel design. A topical report was prepared and received generic approval. Furthermore, because the new design improved the plant safety with respect to loss-of-coolant accidents, there was no intervention against its introduction at all sites.

Several other actions were taken to increase the probability of success. The pellet shape was modified to reduce interaction with the cladding. The inspection standards for the Zircaloy cladding were changed to reduce the permissible defects. Irradiated fuel rods with no failures were returned to Vallecitos to be examined for internal initiation of failure. In the meantime, the GE Research Laboratory was studying ways to attack the problem from the inside of the cladding.

Several other backup remedies were under consideration, including the use of fine-motion control rod drives from Germany to eliminate the step power changes produced by the hydraulic control rod drive system. Prototype fine-motion drives were modified to fit GE BWRs and eventually installed in an operating plant. The channel fabrication method was changed from a "swaged-from-round" fabrication process to brake-form channel halves which are welded in an inert atmosphere (see Figure 5.3). This fabrication process results in a dimensionally stable channel free from any residual stress. Within six months, we had a cohesive organization and a "full court press" to resolve all potential issues. *The number of fuel failures was decreasing as the operating recommendations were taking hold.*

> The number of fuel failures was decreasing as the operating recommendations were taking hold.

The president of GE asked for one of his next briefings to be held at the fuel manufacturing plant at Wilmington, North Carolina. After a quick tour of the plant, he kept coming back to regularly spaced and closed small cans located in the yard. He asked what their content was. I replied that they were filled with rejected pellets and that they were spaced to avoid criticality. His next question was about the total worth of that inventory, and my answer was that it was in excess of $50 million. Before his next question, I added that we were trying to get a new facility to recover that uranium and reuse it but that the approval process was slow. That facility was approved within the next two weeks and the facility was completed on a fast-track basis. When I returned to San Jose, my finance manager informed me that the Nuclear Fuel Department was at the top of an inventory list that went to the president every month. As if I was not busy enough, I was sent to an inventory management course held at the GE management school at Crotonville, Connecticut. I enjoyed it and I requested a copy of that monthly inventory report until the recovery facility helped reduce the notoriety of our department.

Once the 8 × 8 fuel design was introduced in the power plants, there was a noticeable drop-off in fuel failures and the projection was that the reliability goal would be satisfied if our operating rules were retained during the transition period and preferably beyond the time of full 8 × 8 reactor cores. In the meantime there was also significant progress on the research front. *The root cause of fuel pellet cladding interaction failure was identified as internal stress corrosion cracking due to the presence of gaseous fission products, high stresses, and susceptible cladding.* The development of a barrier between cladding and pellets was initiated and patented. It was to come to fruition a few years later to provide the ability to reduce and even eliminate the operating recommendations.

One year into the program, there was a request to make a new estimate of the warranty reserves for the fuel business. The Beaton estimate was calculated to decrease by at least an order of magnitude with conservative assumptions but, in the typical GE financial strategy, the decision was made to increase the warranty reserves until there was more proof of the new projection. The interest of GE top management decreased at that point and I had more time to deal with other responsibilities of my position.

GE was involved in two international joint ventures to manufacture nuclear fuel and was reaching agreement on a third arrangement. The

Figure 5.3.   New fuel channel process using brake-form channel halves.
(Courtesy of General Electric)

oldest joint venture was with AEG in Germany. When AEG's nuclear business was absorbed by Siemens, GE participation decreased from the original 50 percent to a minority role. The second joint venture was in Japan with Toshiba and Hitachi, where GE had maintained its ownership at 50 percent and provided two of the top managers of that facility. The third venture under consideration was in Italy with Ansaldo and it had reached the point of looking for a suitable site. I was expected to attend the board meetings of the joint ventures and be the GE spokesperson. This part of the job offered opportunities to relax because the decisions were made before leaving San Jose. In the case of Japan, the minutes of the meeting were nearly written before the board assembled.

The only decision that had to be made after my arrival was in the case of selecting a site in Italy. Ansaldo had notified GE that they had negotiated very favorable conditions for an undeveloped site in the hills and, upon arrival at the site, I noticed two men standing near the center of the site and arguing loudly and using their arms and hands to reinforce their views. When I reached them, I was informed that they could not agree about the seismic findings of previously taken soil samples. They were both seismic experts, one working for the regulators and the other for Ansaldo. As they tried to convince me, the conversation went from English to Italian and it got louder with time. The solution was easy and consisted of requiring a site on flat land with no previous seismic history.

Another of my responsibilities was to deal with the reprocessing plant. When I visited the site, it was obvious that the project was behind schedule and I authorized the size of the personnel to be increased. Also, I found out from Bob Richards, who had helped develop the PUREX process at Hanford, that the Morris plant was going to use a new fluidized bed process. The shocker was that it was checked at Vallecitos but only on a test tube scale. The project had gone beyond the point of no return and the emphasis was put on performing start-up tests at Morris with natural uranium as soon as possible and fixing the process at full scale if necessary (my preferred approach). I put the designer and the developer of the new process, A. B. Carson and B. F. Judson, in charge since they had the most interest in achieving success.

At that time the nuclear plant owners were very interested in plutonium recycling because the Private Nuclear Fuel Ownership bill was terminating the AEC guaranteed buy-back price of plutonium in December 1970. Plutonium (Pu) utilization had become an option considered when discussing the purchase price of a nuclear power plant, and the nuclear systems vendors were stressing their product's ability to close their fuel cycle. GE had established the feasibility of utilizing Pu fuels in BWRs as early as 1966 in a paper (of which I was a co-author) presented at the Commercial Plutonium Fuels Conference. Satisfactory plutonium fuel irradiation was demonstrated by tests sponsored by AEC at the Saxton reactor and the Experimental Boiling Water Reactor at the Argonne National Laboratory. With the assistance of the Edison Electric Institute (EEI), GE was pursuing additional physics critical tests and insertion of Pu fuel in BWR power plants. *There was still one missing and important element to thermal plutonium recycling: a large fabrication facility to demonstrate that the cost of producing plutonium-enriched fuel would be only about 10 to 20 percent more than that for uranium fuel.*

> There was still one missing and important element to thermal plutonium recycling: a large fabrication facility to demonstrate that the cost of producing plutonium-enriched fuel would be only about 10 to 20 percent more than that for uranium fuel.

With the GE reprocessing facility near start-up, the decision was made to prepare an appropriation request to build such a plutonium fabrication facility, which would allow GE to become the only supplier able to close the fuel cycle. I made the presentation to the GE Board of Directors and the request was turned down because of a doubtful return on investment. I suspect that I lost some points with top management for not being more aggressive about profitability. While I was disappointed by that decision, time proved the board to be right due to proliferation concerns by the U.S. government and the abandonment of thermal plutonium recycling.

There were existing plutonium fuel fabrication facilities in Europe and a supply contract was negotiated with Belgonucleaire to obtain their plutonium services if needed. During those negotiations, I had to remind the principals of that company that I could speak French and understand their private exchanges. Jack Newman (a good friend in later years) was serving as the supplier's lawyer and has embellished that story over the years by claiming that I allowed their conversations to continue until the end of negotiations.

During my tenure at the Nuclear Fuel Department, I was surprised by a Westinghouse decision to offer natural uranium below market costs with the purchase of their nuclear systems. That strategy gave them an advantage in nuclear plant evaluations and increased the number of plant orders they received. The GE marketing organization was eager to adopt the same approach but they had to rely on uranium pricing obtained by the Nuclear Fuel Department. Despite the loss of a few orders and several complaints by GE marketing about the ineptness of the Fuel Department to secure low uranium prices *no speculation was allowed on raw materials* because we had no authority to do so. Westinghouse paid for their speculation in later years when uranium prices rose. *The decision to hold firm and rely on prices from uranium suppliers may have been the most important financial contribution I made to the GE fuel business. The resolution of the pellet/cladding interaction problem was another important technical and financial contribution.* The credit for the latter contribution goes to the early actions taken and their validation with time. The development and the design personnel were responsible for the decisions made without a root cause. The manufacturing personnel also participated by modifying their facility and upgrading their quality assurance on a very short schedule. Subsequent final warranty calculations showed that the original warranty was more than adequate to cover the company risks. My role consisted of keeping everybody focused and avoiding being sidetracked. For example, I refused to consider a 9 × 9 fuel design to get a plant order in Germany because of its impact on the difficult ongoing tasks, especially in manufacturing.

Initial startup tests at Morris were not going well and that facility

> The decision to hold firm and rely on prices from uranium suppliers may have been the most important financial contribution I made to the GE fuel business.

What is also remarkable is the lack of attention that was given to how unreasonable the design basis of the APS's presumed large LOCA was. Subsequent probabilistic studies showed that its contribution to risks was negligible in all LWR plants. While the APS study added to the raging debate about the safety of nuclear power, it was also very helpful in initiating many tests and improved analyses by the government and industry. As pointed out in 1988 in NUREG -1230, *Compendium of ECCS Research for Realistic Analyses,* more than $700 million had been spent by 1988 to show that the ECC systems can and will function reliably.

Concerns about the stress corrosion cracking of stainless steel also resurfaced. Instead of implicating furnace-sensitized material, leaks were now occurring in the heat-affected zones of piping due to sensitization from welding heat input. The first case reported was in a highly stressed, cold-worked, 4-inch piping bypass around a water circulating pipe at the Dresden plant. *The cause of that first piping failure was determined to be very high stresses due to poor design. Insufficient attention was given to residual stresses due to poor welding practices, which produced leaks in large pipes several years later.* The stresses were lower and took longer to penetrate the increased thickness of large pipes. They also were uncovered in the thermal sleeves of piping because they could form crevices to concentrate impurities.

> The cause of that first piping failure was determined to be very high stresses due to poor design.

Dr. Klepfer was asked to assemble a group of independent experts to assess the root cause of the failures and means to correct them. A comprehensive review report was prepared and issued to the regulators and all the BWR owners. *The remedies included using stainless steel with less carbon content, decreasing the heat input during welding, and providing water cooling during the welding process to reduce residual stresses.* Significant contributions were made to the program by the GE Research Laboratory. A weld-overlay method also was developed to allow continued use of the original piping. A large enough weld overlay was applied to the weld heat-affected zone to satisfy the applicable ASME codes. The search for improved materials was not stopped because the research was close to identifying improved and alternate materials.

During my assignment in the Nuclear Fuel Department, the Mark II containment came under attack as in the case of the Mark I for providing insufficient space for maintenance. Development Engineering had developed a new design using sets of three circular holes located at the bottom of the drywell and a very large annular pool. The wetwell was a large domed circular structure of high volume operating at a reduced pressure with respect to PWR dry containment. This new model was referred to as MARK III and the reactor associated with it was the BWR-6 (see Figure 5.4). It had a power output of 1300 MWe, the maximum authorized by the regulators. There was no change in the fuel peak specific power; the power output increase resulted from a decrease in peaking factors by making the water gap the same size around the periphery of the fuel channel.

Consideration was given to meeting the European requirement for full load rejection by increasing the number of relief valves and having the additional valves handle the short-term excess steam produced by full load rejection. The GE licensees in Japan preferred to enlarge their Mark II containment design rather than have an open pool, as in the case of the Mark III design, and have to face the small possibility of radioactivity being released from defective fuel in the pool. At home, there was a big push to sell the BWR-6, and several plant orders were received. Those were the last domestic orders obtained by GE and other vendors.

During the development of the Mark I containment, the tests had emphasized the ability to condense the steam to avoid containment overpressure failures. The tests were performed with different pipe sizes and water depths. The experiments showed that complete condensation would happen as long as the water depth was not so small that steam could escape before being fully condensed. There were vibrations when the pool temperature reached about 170°F and design features (increased pool size and reduced initial temperature) were implemented to avoid this region. There were no measurements of loads on structures and the conclusion was reached that the loads were not large because

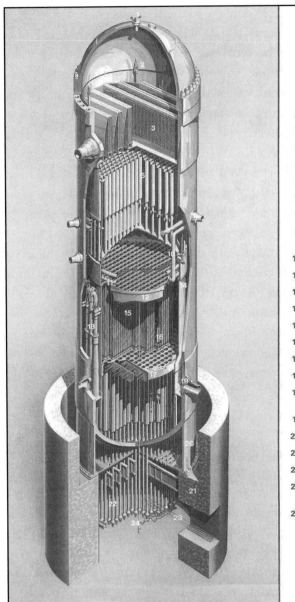

BWR/6
REACTOR ASSEMBLY

1. VENT AND HEAD SPRAY
2. STEAM DRYER LIFTING LUG
3. STEAM DRYER ASSEMBLY
4. STEAM OUTLET
5. CORE SPRAY INLET
6. STEAM SEPARATOR ASSEMBLY
7. FEEDWATER INLET
8. FEEDWATER SPARGER
9. LOW PRESSURE COOLANT INJECTION INLET
10. CORE SPRAY LINE
11. CORE SPRAY SPARGER
12. TOP GUIDE
13. JET PUMP ASSEMBLY
14. CORE SHROUD
15. FUEL ASSEMBLIES
16. CONTROL BLADE
17. CORE PLATE
18. JET PUMP / RECIRCULATION WATER INLET
19. RECIRCULATION WATER OUTLET
20. VESSEL SUPPORT SKIRT
21. SHIELD WALL
22. CONTROL ROD DRIVES
23. CONTROL ROD DRIVE HYDRAULIC LINES
24. IN-CORE FLUX MONITOR

GENERAL ⊕ ELECTRIC

Figure 5.4. BWR-6 reactor assembly associated with the Mark III containment system. (Courtesy of General Electric)

they did not cause any visible damage to the test facility.

No new tests were necessary for the Mark II design because the pipe sizes and water depths had been covered under the Mark I program. The Mark III design configuration, however, was quite different and a new facility was built. It was equipped with a variety of new instruments to obtain structural data and to take movies. Because the Mark III pool was open, it was possible to observe pool swell, as shown in Figure 5.5, after the steam/water/air mixture reaches the suppression pool. Structures located within the path of the swell were subjected to impact loads and some had to be moved upward. Also, some of the bottom pool water did not participate in the condensation process and the pool temperature maldistribution needed to be taken into account.

Those results had an influence on the Mark I and II containments. Vermont Yankee in Connecticut was the first plant to perform preliminary analyses of loads and to find out that the Mark I containment might no longer satisfy the applicable ASME codes. The regulators, however, allowed continued operation of the power plants by using some of the large ASME code safety margins and a reduced initial containment pressure, if necessary. A commitment was made to perform tests to measure the prevailing loads and to use them to modify the designs to satisfy applicable codes.

Phil Bray had become responsible for all the GE nuclear projects and their licensing. He arranged for GE to participate in a Mark I owners group and to pay an appropriate share of the study costs to cover the plants for which GE was responsible (within GE scope and under warranty). Due to potential conflict of interest, GE was not allowed to bid on the Mark I test facility and the reduction and analyses of the data. Consultants were hired to provide guidance and *many management decisions were slow because they were made by a committee, which should be avoided.* There was also financial tension between GE and owners with plants beyond warranty. I was frustrated by the Mark I working conditions but I tried hard to abide by them.

When the load problem did spread to the Mark II design, a different approach was adopted. A test facility was paid for and built by GE at San Jose on a very short schedule by expensing it and avoiding a long

Figure 5.5.   Mark III open suppression pool. (Source: author observation)

company approval process. Pool swell data were obtained quickly and an analytical model was generated by Dr. Fred Moody for licensing purposes. At the same time, experiments were being carried out in

Germany about the opening of relief valves in the much smaller suppression water pools used in German BWRs. That program was initiated after a relief valve was operated several times in a German power plant and the pool temperature was allowed to exceed the GE limit of 170°F, which produced the large vibrations observed in the initial tests of the Mark I design. To reduce the loads from opening relief valves, quenchers consisting of exhaust horizontal piping with very small holes were developed. The condensation of the steam escaping through small holes was shown to reduce the loads by about an order of magnitude and Pio Ianni, who was in charge of the GE loads program, favored their introduction into GE BWRs.

Brian Webster, the project manager for international plants, needed immediate load decisions and insisted that they should be conservative to avoid future changes. Pio Ianni prepared a set of recommendations for my signature, including strengthening the supports of the steam downcomers, tacking the steel liner to the containment concrete structure, and adding quenchers to the relief valve piping. That combination of changes could cope with potential load combinations and it was implemented on international plants. I presented the same action plan to the U.S. owners group and urged its adoption. The owners decided to continue their protracted discussions with regulators. That strategy resulted in a long time passing before agreement was reached on a set of containment loads, which delayed completion of final designs and construction. Due to the high inflation rate prevailing then, plant costs ballooned.

The demand for reactor pressure vessels exceeded the U.S. supply, so some orders were placed in foreign countries. For example, the vessels for the Browns Ferry units were placed in Holland with Rotterdam Dry Dock. Chicago Bridge & Iron (CBI), however, had built pressure vessels for small BWRs in the field and their quality and schedule performance was excellent. They had a facility in Memphis, Tennessee, which could be upgraded and enlarged to meet GE projected needs of six to seven pressure vessels per year. So a joint venture, called CBIN for CBI Nuclear, was put together; additional buildings were added and machining equipment ordered to meet the GE objective (see Figure 5.6).

Figure 5.6. The CBIN joint venture plant in Memphis, Tennessee.
(Source: CBIN brochure)

CBIN ownership was 50/50 and there was a breakup clause that allowed each partner to put in a bid for the partner share. The highest bidder would own the entire facility. That clause was never used because the parties were able to work together. CBI was in charge of the production, while the finance manager was from GE. The chairman of the venture was the president of CBI. I was the vice chairman and Bill Oberly who was responsible for the GE purchase of equipment was also on the CBIN board. A CBI senior vice president completed the board membership. Regular board meetings were held and the production and financial status covered.

An important innovation was introduced when the decision was made to install all BWR internals at the Memphis CBIN plant. The quality of the installation and its cost improved. There was only one difficult moment at the joint venture when the amount of natural gas available for welding and heat treatment was being limited under the Carter administration. CBI suggested importing liquefied natural gas; GE personnel, recognizing the small chance of getting headquarters to approve the ownership of natural gas, suggested a development program to reduce the use of natural gas. That program was very successful because it reduced the fabrication costs while remaining within the prescribed natural gas quotas. Several years later, the CBIN buildings were filled with completed pressure vessels kept in storage due to delays or cancellations of BWR projects.

The AEC had been accused of having a conflict of interest because it was promoting nuclear power at the same time that it was regulating it. In 1974, the AEC was abolished and the Nuclear Regulatory Commission (NRC) was created to regulate nuclear power. The formation of the NRC opened the process to public participation and increased the formality of licensing submittals and hearings, with lawyers playing a big role in the issuance and review of documents and presentations. That was a favorable development as far as opening the process to the public except in those cases where the sole objective of the intervention was to stop a project licensing by any means. *In my opinion, the time required to obtain a construction permit or an operating license about doubled under the new NRC process and nuclear plant costs increased sharply due to prevailing high inflation and interest rates during the delays.*

Many plant owners continued to assume that they could recover their costs and pass them to their customers as long as the project was approved by their state energy commission. As the number and size of requested regulated rate adjustments increased, some states looked into their validity and the topic of inadequate management was used to disallow several rate increases. That practice spread and it led to project delays, cancellations, and eventually no new orders although the management problem was not the only reason for these changes.

During my assignment at the BWR Systems Department, I first reported to George Stathakis but that arrangement was changed so I worked for John Selby as did the people in Manufacturing. Marketing and Projects reported to George Stathakis. That split increased the tension between Stathakis and Selby. Also, the containment load concerns did not help the division's financial performance and another independent review of the nuclear business was initiated.

Charlie Reed headed the review and he was supported by a team of the best engineers at GE. Henry Stone, who had left KAPL to join the Nuclear Division as head of Strategic Planning, became a member of the review team and kept us posted on the ongoing deliberations. Based on the recommendation of John Selby, I had hired Dr. Frank Judge to look after the engineering work output for all GE plants. Frank was tough but fair and he did not hesitate to make the difficult decisions. I had promoted Don Rubio to become the general manager of the Control and Instrumentation Department. Don had taken over my position of manager of the Design Engineering Section when I was promoted to run the fuel business.

I spent two full days in Florida with the Reed task force and I described the potential problems and answered numerous questions. I asked Don Rubio to handle a follow-up session. Members of the task force also came to San Jose and were given full access to the engineers doing the work. It was becoming apparent that there would be another change in division management once the Reed report was published. John Selby had hoped to get the top job, but just in case, he also looked at other available positions. Not too long after, John Selby announced that he had agreed to become the president of Consumers Power Company, which was in a protracted fight to license a large dual-purpose nuclear power plant in Michigan (the plant was not licensed due to intervention). George Stathakis appointed me to replace John Selby and to become the general manager of BWR Operations in early 1975.

BWR OPERATIONS

I was now in charge of all the engineering and manufacturing for GE nuclear power plants and I had about 4000 employees reporting to me. Roy Beaton was named to head the Nuclear Division and I shared a secretary and a suite of offices with him to provide immediate status and feedback on items of interest to headquarters. Dr. Beaton was easy to work for. He wanted to be kept informed and not to be surprised. He passed me handwritten notes on his topics of interest and was provided answers right away on the same sheet of paper. Henry Stone was appointed to take over the BWR Systems Department and he and Frank Judge handled the day-to-day engineering problems.

The Reed task force had raised several issues and a full response was prepared for Beaton review and for later transmittal to Ed Hood and headquarters. One of the key findings was that *Engineering did not control changes to BWR models. To correct that situation, a Configuration Control Board (CCB) was created* and I chaired all of the meetings. Marketing and Projects were members of the CCB. Product changes were not approved without acceptance by Engineering. Costs and schedules for implementation were developed ahead of the review and minutes were prepared. Another concern of the task force was that some changes were being implemented before full verification in the field. *The success of the steam turbine-generator and aircraft jet engine divisions was being attributed to their ability to test their products at full scale before they were sold.* That strategy could not work for BWR power plants because of the very high cost associated with a prototype (at least $1 billion), long schedule (above 6 years), and required regulatory approval. Instead, *in retrospect, the approach had been to test full-scale modules such as the fuel assembly, jet pump, steam separator, control rod drive, and to check their assembly through extensive power plant start-up tests. Also, many of the problems would not have been detected in plant prototypes because they were long-life materials issues, balance-of-plant problems outside GE's scope, and changes in regulations.* The Reed report made many recommendations and periodic reports were prepared for progress purposes. The NRC was given a proprietary copy of the original Reed report to show that no new safety issues were being raised.

We had been told repeatedly to follow the pattern of the steam turbine generator division and we did. The Reed task force had rejected the addition of relief valves for full load rejection and a full load bypass was designed and installed by Brown-Boveri for the Leibstadt plant in Switzerland. Similarly, we did not partici-

> Many of the problems would not have been detected in plant prototypes because they were long-life materials issues, balance-of-plant problems outside GE's scope, and changes in regulations.

pate in the design and installation of a fully safeguarded independent shutdown cooling system because it was not included in our standard design. Marketing was trying to close the sale of the Kaiseraugst plant in Switzerland, and Ed Hood, the senior vice president of power systems, participated in those final negotiations. The agreement was to supply a combination of BWR-5 and BWR-6 features but that concept was rejected by the Configuration Control Board. That decision was not well received by Ed Hood even though I was following his instructions and the compromise was to have the engineering office in Switzerland carry out the work without involvement from San Jose (that plant was eventually canceled due to local intervention). Manufacturing at Wilmington, which had reported to John Selby, continued to hint about becoming a product business. That may have been a good suggestion but at the wrong time and the manager of Manufacturing was replaced. After interviews with several candidates, Dr. Beaton and I selected Randy Alkema for that position. Randy came from the steam turbine division and understood the importance of working as a team with Engineering.

Those were busy days and they became hectic when *three GE engineers decided to resign and attack the safety and the quality of the work they were involved with.* The leader was Dale Bridenbaugh who worked for Phil Bray and was in charge of the containment loads project. The second member was named Hubbard and he was responsible for the quality assurance of the Control and Instrumentation Department. The third participant was a young engineer who designed advance control rooms. Their announcement received considerable attention in the local and national news and a special session of Congress was held to hear their concerns. Phil Bray and I were asked to respond to the issues raised. We were given a copy of their presentation late the night before their meeting with Congress members the following day. It was clear that they had spent considerable time preparing their material and they most likely had received a lot of outside writing help. Phil and I spent several hours preparing a potential response.

The next day, the hearing room was full of press and television personnel and the three engineers were given full opportunity to state their case without giving us the chance to respond to their claims. We were rescheduled for a later session and returned home where the decision was made not to attack the dissidents. (For example, I had received the latest monthly quality assurance report by Hubbard and it was quite positive in contrast to his statements after his resignation.) The emphasis was instead put on describing our detailed approach to safety in design, manufacturing, construction, quality assurance, independent reviews, and testing of GE nuclear products. *On our return to the congressional session, we were surprised by the absence of most previous congressional members and the lack of any member from the press or television.* After the hearings, the three engineers continued to attack the nuclear industry while they offered consulting services to domestic state energy commissions that were opposing nuclear plant cost increases, and to foreign countries such as Sweden, which was considering putting a halt to future nuclear plant construction. Dr. Beaton and I had to visit one GE customer to confirm that GE employees could voice their safety concerns. In fact, there was a top-level policy allowing nuclear employees to submit any safety concern they had and to have management respond to it.

Soc Roumanis from the Control and Instrumentation Department had developed a power generation control complex (PGCC). *The PGCC applied factory packaging to the manner in which nuclear control equipment was supplied and installed at power plants.* It simplified equipment setup, field interconnections, and testing. GE received several orders for that design, resulting in a need for enlarged control room fabrication facilities. When a facility request was submitted to cover our needs, we were asked to look at two available manufacturing buildings. The first one was in Syracuse, New York, and the second one was in South Carolina. The Syracuse plant was used to build televisions, but it had been shut down due to severe union difficulties. The South Carolina facility was a very plush, new facility and would become the subject of customer criticism and a financial burden to the Control and Instrumentation Department. In the end, neither facility was chosen; instead, in a decision that ran contrary to headquarters' wishes, a warehouse-type facility in San Jose was leased for *co-locating manufacturing and engineering personnel in San Jose for the PGCC business.* That choice was made because of the difficulties encountered in the fuel business due to the long distance separating engineering and manufacturing. (At that time, a fast means of communication was not yet available.)

In March 1975, there was a significant fire at Browns Ferry.

In March 1975, there was a significant fire at Browns Ferry. That fire started when a lighted candle was used to detect possible leaks and caused flammable material to burn. The fire was extinguished with water by local firemen. The fuel was kept covered with water at all times by using the limited control rod drive flow of 200 gallons per minute. The investigation showed that the *requirements for separation were not implemented properly and that the power produced in a few power cables may have been excessive.* The event led to increased requirements by the NRC for means to terminate fires, to separate safety equipment, and to control power generation in cable conduits. Henry Stone was responsible for the resolution of the Browns Ferry fire, including the many phone calls received at night when the plant was being stabilized. *I still remember participating in the NOVA recounting of that event and I regret giving the producers the exclusive right to select its content because their choice of my statements did not do justice to my views.*

There was another field experience that is worth recounting. Water in BWRs was being supplied outside the fuel channels to avoid the presence of steam in that region and to cool the in-core chambers located inside the instrument tube. Holes were provided in the bottom reactor core plate to allow the right amount of water to reach the space between channels. *The water velocity leaving the holes was too high and caused the instrument tubes to vibrate and perforate the fuel channels.* The core plate holes were closed with spring-loaded plugs and small holes were added to the bottom support structure of each fuel assembly.

Again, Henry Stone's team of engineers implemented the modification to obtain a reduced and much more uniform flow between channels. I inherited the job of explaining the problem at the Duane Arnold BWR in Iowa and to the Japanese authorities. The press conference in Iowa with the participation of NRC went very well. The presentation in Japan stopped abruptly when I stated that this was a temporary fix and that GE was looking at alternates. I was told that Japan could not accept a temporary fix and that I should come back when GE had a permanent fix. On my return to San Jose, the engineers went to work and showed that the fix had a long enough life to be considered permanent according to accepted ASME codes. *I have since stricken the word* temporary *from my vocabulary when in Japan.*

GE appears to operate on a three-year cycle for reorganization and I was approached for suggestions about changes in the summer of 1977. I indicated that the prevailing organization was too much one over one and that different structures should be examined. A few weeks later, I was advised that Dr. Roy Beaton would be promoted to senior vice president and would have two vice presidents report to him and that I would have first choice to become vice president of Engineering or Manufacturing. I declined both positions and resigned from GE.

My primary reason for resigning was that I was afraid that my new job would be less challenging and not as enjoyable—until now, GE had always promoted me from a challenging position to a more challenging one. A secondary reason was that I wanted to try an academic position or become a consultant instead of having to go from crisis to crisis. Reg Jones and Ed Hood offered to see me before my decision became final but I refused their offer. B. Satterlee, who was in charge of Human Relations, put a set of numbers together showing the economic

THE INDISPENSABLE MAN

Sometime when you're feeling important.
Sometime when your ego's in bloom.
Sometime when you take it for granted
You're the best qualified in the room.
Sometime when you feel that your going
Would leave an unfillable hole.
Just follow this simple instruction
And see how it humbles your soul:

Take a bucket and fill it with water
Put your hand in it up to the wrist.
Pull it out and the hole that's remaining
Is a measure of how you'll be missed.
You may splash all you please when you enter
You may stir up the water galore.
But stop and you'll find in a minute
That it looks quite the same as before.

The moral in this quaint example.
Is do just the best you can.
Be proud of yourself but remember....
There's no Indispensable man.
                              —Author Unknown

Figure 5.7. CBIN "memorandum" on the "indispensable" man. (Source: CBIN board member)

advantages I would gain if I stayed with GE until age 55 but I did not look at them. I wanted to leave GE in a very friendly manner and the attendance at my going-away assembly and the numerous supportive letters I received confirmed that I was leaving many friends behind. The memorandum received from CBIN (reproduced in Figure 5.7) was especially helpful for keeping my ego under control. As stated in that memo, *I just did the best I could.* When Dr. Beaton found out that I had resigned without having another position, he gave me a consulting contract to advise Bill Anders, the astronaut and the new vice president of Manufacturing. I was even more surprised when Dr. Beaton asked me to visit him in April 1978 and handed me a very large incentive compensation check for my work in 1977 and stated that I had earned it fully. For the first time in my career, my wife was concerned about my decision. So was I but I tried hard not to show it.

SIX

RETROSPECTIVE OF NUCLEAR POWER GENERATION OF ELECTRICITY IN 1977–1978

BACKGROUND

Controlled nuclear fission reactions were first utilized to produce plutonium for nuclear weapons, the first of which was set off by the United States on July 16, 1945. It did not take long after that momentous event to establish the U.S. Atomic Energy Commission (AEC) in 1946. The AEC formed a civilian and a naval branch to pursue the application of nuclear energy to the production of electricity and the development of long-term propulsion of submarines, cruisers, and aircraft carriers, respectively. The first submarine, *Nautilus*, which used a pressurized water reactor (PWR), went to sea in 1955. It is sufficient to report here that the nuclear navy program was very successful and received the full support of the president, Congress, and the public. Even though there was some opposition to nuclear vessels entering certain ports, I am not aware of any opposition to that program that matched the difficulties encountered by the civilian nuclear generation of electricity. I am also not aware of any study to understand why the nuclear navy and civilian electricity programs received such different political and public acceptance.

Initially, exuberance about the nuclear power generation of electricity was unlimited because it was found that more than two neutrons could be released per fission collision event. This meant that enormous amounts of energy or "all of the world's electricity for hundred of years could be produced" according to Fermi (Koch, L. J., *Nuclear News,* October 2002) if those fission reactions were at high energy. It was presumed that thermal reactors such as light water reactors (LWRs) would generate plutonium (Pu) and would reprocess their fuel to separate Pu and recycle it in thermal reactors or in reactors of high energy, called breeders, because they could produce more Pu than they would consume. The Civilian Branch of AEC, with strong support from the Joint Committee on Atomic Energy (JCAE), pursued a vigorous program to generate electricity from nuclear reactors. At first, the breeder reactor received major attention because of concern about the availability of uranium. The first Experimental Breeder Reactor, EBR-1, reached full power on December 19, 1951. It was the first reactor to generate electricity and to produce more Pu than the fissionable U-235 that it consumed.

On December 8, 1953, at a plenary meeting of the United Nations, President Dwight D. Eisenhower launched the Atoms for Peace initiative, which provided for sharing of substantial nuclear technology for peaceful purposes with countries willing to forego nuclear weapons development. A total of 187 nations have signed the Treaty on the Non-Proliferation of Nuclear Weapons (NPT) and the International Atomic Energy Agency (IAEA) was formed to monitor adherence to the NPT and to assist in the transfer of technology.

The complex and essentially political nature of nuclear proliferation had not yet been fully resolved.

The Atoms for Peace program allowed additional countries to have access to the equipment, materials, and technology necessary for the manufacture of nuclear weapons, that is, facilities for separation of Pu and enrichment of uranium. Note that not all nations signed the NPT or foreswore nuclear weapons development and 25 years after President Eisenhower's speech, *the complex and essentially political nature of nuclear proliferation had not yet been fully resolved.* In an article in the November 8, 1977, issue of the

Wall Street Journal, H. S. Rowen called the Atoms for Peace program "one of the most mindless undertakings in the annals of American government." That judgment is wrong because it presumed that other countries would not be able to develop nuclear power with its potential for producing weapons. It was bound to happen as a matter of time. With the Atoms for Peace program, the spread of weapons technology would be much more monitored and much less certain to occur.

In 1954, the AEC initiated a Power Reactor Development Program that led to the design, construction, and operation of several thermal reactors. Two winners emerged from that major effort: the pressurized water reactor (PWR) and the boiling water reactor (BWR). The first demonstration PWR was Westinghouse's Shippingport, Pennsylvania, plant, which produced 60 MWe in December 1957. It was followed by Yankee Rowe in Massachusetts, which generated 167 MWe on November 1960, and Indian Point 1 (Buchanan, New York), which reached 257 MWe on January 1963, and so on.

The first BWR was the Experimental Boiling Water Reactor (EBWR), which generated 5 MWe in December 1956 at the Argonne National Laboratory (ANL). The Vallecitos BWR near Pleasanton, California, was next and it received the first power reactor license on November 25, 1957. It was followed by Dresden 1 in Illinois, which produced 180 MWe in July 1960, and so on. According to a Ford Foundation Study, in mid-1976, "Nuclear power plants in the U.S. accounted for about 40,000 MWe. Some 170,000 MWe of additional nuclear capacity were scheduled to begin operation by mid-1980s. Projections for the year 2000 ranged from about 400,000 to 600,000 MWe."

With respect to the breeder reactor program, it remained primarily under the purview of the U.S. government. EBR-1 was shut down by a meltdown accident in 1955 but was operational again in less than nine months. In 1963, EBR-2 reached criticality and produced 16.5 MWe. It was shut down eventually in 1994 by U.S. government directive. The only other planned U.S. demonstration breeder reactor was the Clinch River Breeder Reactor (CRBR), which was initiated in 1972 but never reached the construction stage with much of the major components fabricated.

In 1974, the AEC was abolished and the Nuclear Regulatory Commission (NRC) was created to regulate nuclear power. The Energy Research and Development Administration (ERDA) became responsible for energy development including nuclear power. JCAE stopped existing after the demise of the AEC and congressional responsibility for nuclear power became more diffuse and much more political and partisan.

In October 1975, the Reactor Safety Study (WASH-1400) was published. It was a comprehensive probabilistic assessment of the risks associated with nuclear reactor accidents. Its purpose was to show that nuclear accident risks compared favorably with other forms of energy and it did a remarkable job of supporting that conclusion.

In 1977, a Ford Foundation-sponsored evaluation on "Nuclear Power Issues and Choices" (Nuclear Energy Policy Study Group, ISBN 0-88410-065-0, Ballinger Publishing Company, 1977) was initiated because "the public debate on nuclear power issues was poorly structured and undisciplined. The various actors were talking past each other to the crowd, irresponsible statements were going unchallenged, and implicit value judgments were unacknowledged." The report contains extensive and valuable information about the status of nuclear power up to 1977–1978 and is quoted frequently in this chapter.

By late 1977, no new domestic orders were being placed for nuclear power plants. Instead, delays or cancellations of previous orders were happening. The start of this reversal can be traced to "the oil embargo of 1973 and the subsequent large increase in OPEC oil prices," which produced an economic recession and reduced the projections for electricity growth. The dearth of orders in 1977 and beyond is due to many other reasons and the purpose of this retrospective is to understand those circumstances. The following causes will be examined:

- Capital costs and the duration of projects,
- Regulatory licensing,
- Safety,
- The politics of nuclear proliferation, and
- The institutional framework.

CAPITAL COSTS AND
THE DURATION OF PROJECTS

The costs of nuclear power depend most on the capital costs of the plant and the time taken from the start of the project to reaching warranted output. The capital costs of nuclear power nearly doubled from 1970 to 1976 and they continued to rise thereafter. The reasons are that the original estimates were low and the manpower requirements in man-hours per kilowatt for construction nearly doubled from 1970 to 1976. Also, the field labor rate increased due to high inflation after the oil embargo of 1973 and the lack of experienced field personnel. *Another important contributor was the poor completion of engineering when construction started.* The Ford Foundation report claims that "engineering was about 2 percent complete when construction began on the first TVA plant." There were also big changes to the design before it was ready for operation. For example, cooling towers were added to satisfy environmental concerns; applicable seismic levels were increased; and new requirements were introduced for fire separation and equipment qualification to cope with a radioactive environment in the event of a severe accident. Another factor was the increased duration of nuclear power projects, which went from 5 years in 1960 to about 10 years in 1977–1978.

The NRC opened the regulatory process to public hearings, which was a good idea but it allowed the participation of parties intent only on halting nuclear progress. It added, on average, about a one-year delay each for getting a construction or an operating permit. *Another serious shortcoming was the lack of strong talent to manage large and complex projects.* The most flagrant case was the five nuclear power plants being constructed by the Washington Power Plant Supply System (WPPSS), in which each plant used a different design and was managed by different subtier contractors. For example, piping subcontractors received little supervision and forced the abandonment of four projects and the lengthy shutdown of the fifth power plant. *Quality assurance problems surfaced heavily in the field*—often very late in the construction process—which encour-

> Another serious shortcoming was the lack of strong talent to manage large and complex projects.

aged abandonment of a few plants rather than facing the difficult task of repeating the inspection tests.

During that time, a jump occurred in interest rates. Rates jumped from "about 8 percent of capital costs for plants going into commercial service in 1972 to about 20 percent for those going into service in 1983." Also, the original expectations were far from being met for plant capacity factor and the size of the staff needed to operate new plants.

Fortunately, some of the above impacts were attenuated by increased power outputs (from 500 to 1300 MWe) and reduced nuclear fuel costs due to increased fuel burnup. Also, coal plant capital costs were being subjected to similar increased economics but at a reduced rate. The conclusion of the Ford Foundation report was that "the costs of power generation in the Midwest may be about equal for nuclear and coal-generated power." However, whether it was a nuclear or coal power plant, it was not easy to face the state regulatory body and explain how and why costs have doubled from the original estimate in a span of six years.

REGULATORY LICENSING

In the early days of the development of nuclear power, regulators were swamped by the number of applications and the shortage of experienced regulators. The use of the defense-in-depth concept to safeguard the barriers that were designed to stop the release of fission products and the introduction of technical specifications for plant operations were excellent ideas for ensuring safety. However, a lack of well-defined criteria, escalation of the number of regulations, and regulation inconsistencies over time made it difficult to get a license in a reasonable time period.

The amount of material to be submitted and the number of questions to be answered in writing kept growing. The regulatory supervisors and managers were reluctant to provide guidance to their staff in order to avoid the same issues being raised several times. Because project delays raised plant costs, many plant owners were inclined to make concessions and changes to the design. Cost/benefit and probabilistic analyses were seldom accepted to settle differences of opinion. In summary, the licensing process was much like an "obstacle course" with great uncertainties about reaching its end. *The regulatory process needed stability and predictability* for increased assurance of success to "avoid delays and increased costs".

The regulatory process needed stability and predictability.

SAFETY

The safety of nuclear power plants has remained an issue because the consequences of a major and severe reactor accident could be quite serious. For that reason, nuclear power plants are regulated and they require the submittal of licensee event reports (LERs), which tend to be reported by the media and raise public concern even when some are trivial.

Also, independent safety evaluations have not always helped public acceptance. For example, the tests conducted in 1972 in the small semi-scale, electrically heated facility at Idaho Falls fall into that category because, due to poor scaling, they indicated that injected emergency cooling water might not reach the reactor core. In addition, the results were announced prematurely. Similarly, the independent review by the American Physical Society in 1974 of LWR safety concluded that the "probability of emergency core cooling systems functioning was unpredictable." That statement should have had the qualifier "under extremely low probability conditions," as supported by the WASH-1400 study published in 1975.

There is no question, however, that nuclear power plants need continued and strong vigilance to ensure their safe operation and that the American Physical Society study helped launch extensive studies of emergency cooling behavior to understand the expected phenomena and their prediction. When the Ford Foundation study looked at the safety of nuclear power, it applied a conservative factor of 500 for potential uncertainties to the WASH-1400 calculated rate of loss and it still found that nuclear power rate of loss stayed below the range of coal power plants. *It is clear that the attitude toward the safety of nuclear power plants has improved only as the years of continued safe operation have increased.*

THE POLITICS OF NUCLEAR PROLIFERATION

According to the Ford Foundation report, "the most serious risk associated with nuclear power is the attendant increase in the number of countries that have access to technology, materials, and facilities (Pu reprocessing and recycling and uranium enrichment) leading to a nuclear weapons capability." That risk was recognized under the Atoms for Peace program of 1953 and led to the NPT and the formation of the IAEA. Under those arrangements, nonweapons states were given access to nuclear power technology if they would forego nuclear weapons. That strategy was not foolproof because it allowed a few NPT and non-NPT signatories (e.g., India, Pakistan, Israel, and China) to develop and test nuclear weapons. In 1977, H. S. Rowen estimated that there were "around 40 countries—some unstable, some engaged in intense regional disputes—capable within a decade of acquiring nuclear explosives." Today, that concern has increased due to terrorist activities and the more readily available knowledge about the small and less costly centrifuge enrichment technology.

As noted in the Ford Foundation report, "the solution lies in comprehensive and broader political actions and international arrangements to contain nuclear weapon proliferation." The most complete statement about this topic was made by Senator Sam Nunn in his introduction to the 2004 book *A Brighter Tomorrow,* by Senator Pete V. Domenici. It proposes that

> [W]e need a system of global nuclear materials management in which all nuclear materials are safe, secure, and accounted for from cradle to grave with sufficient transparency to assure the world that this is the case. Nuclear material security, nonproliferation, and safe nuclear power plants and waste disposal procedures all form a chain that must be unbreakable if the world is to realize the full potential of nuclear power in cleaning our air and closing the gap between the world's haves and have-nots."

The lack of such a solution is still with us today. Interestingly, in the *Wall Street Journal* on January 4, 2007, former Secretaries of State George P. Shultz and Henry A. Kissinger, former Secretary of Defense William

J. Perry, and Senator Sam Nunn suggested a return to "continuing to reduce substantially the size of nuclear forces in all states that possess them." Their vision of "a world free of nuclear weapons," however, may take considerable time to achieve.

Initially, the AEC encouraged thermal recycling of plutonium and the development of a breeder reactor. In 1966, Milton Shaw, director of the AEC's Division of Reactor Technology and Development, presented a paper titled "AEC Programs and Requirements for Plutonium" at the Commercial Plutonium Fuels Conference in March 1966, which I attended. Shaw described the extensive government development efforts regarding the use of plutonium in thermal reactors and stated that "the basic questions of feasibility have been answered and a large body of experience, data, and design information has been developed." He pointed out that "2400 plutonium enriched rods have been irradiated in the Plutonium Recycle Test Reactor (PRTR), 1200 rods are presently in the EBWR, and 640 rods are in the Saxton reactor." The plans called for completion of several programs by 1970 and phase-out of the AEC funding for the thermal recycling program by that time.

In that same talk, Shaw noted that "it is essential that an economic, reliable, and safe fast breeder system be developed together with the requisite industrial capabilities." Also, in 1966 the AEC authorized the operation of the first private reprocessing plant by Nuclear Fuel Services (NFS). The plant operated until 1972 when it was shut down for improvement and enlargement. Two other reprocessing plants were under construction: a smaller GE demonstration plant at Morris, Illinois, and a large one at Barnwell, South Carolina, by Allied Chemical. They never started up and the NFS plant never returned to service because the U.S. position on reprocessing changed dramatically during the campaign for the presidency in 1976. During his campaign, Jimmy Carter stated that he would "seek to withhold authority for domestic reprocessing until the need for the economics and the safety of this technology is clearly demonstrated." On October 28, 1976, President Ford announced that "reprocessing and recycling of plutonium should not proceed unless there is sound reason to conclude that the world community can overcome effectively the associated risk of proliferation." Those statements were made with the hope that other countries would follow the U.S. position of not reprocessing, but it did not happen because such energy resource–poor countries as France, India, and Japan could not and would not abandon the use of plutonium as a source of energy. The U.S. position had not been based on a real assessment of international preferences.

The Ford Foundation evaluation issued in 1977 agreed with the presidential positions and concluded the following:

> Reprocessing and recycle are not essential to nuclear power; reprocessing of spent fuel, even on a demonstration basis, should be deferred as a matter of national policy, until it is clearly necessary on a national scale; there is little advantage in terms of economics or energy supply assurance in early commercial introduction of Liquid Metal Fast Breeder Reactors (LMFBRs); it is important to continue work on the breeder, with a longer time horizon and an emphasis on its role as insurance; any additional enrichment capacity, whether using gaseous or centrifuge technology, should be built by the government; the government should maintain strict classification and export controls on laser technology; the most important U.S. objective should be, therefore, to develop an international consensus on the problems and risks of a plutonium economy, and to encourage a more cautious approach to plutonium reprocessing and recycle and breeder reactors. Within such a consensus it will be possible to pursue export policies that will inhibit the spread of technologies carrying the most serious proliferation risks, while at the same time ensuring the availability of nuclear power to meet world energy needs.

In retrospect, the U.S. policy on plutonium reprocessing and recycling and the breeder reactor was not consistent over the years.

In retrospect, the U.S. policy on plutonium reprocessing and recycling and the breeder reactor was not consistent over the years because first it encouraged the industry to support their development and to invest considerable funds in facilities and studies and then to abandon them. Also, it failed to develop an international consensus on foolproof means to contain nuclear proliferation in all countries, whether energy resource– poor or –rich. Many other potential measures are suggested in the Ford Foundation study (see page 23 of the study cited earlier) but they are mostly political and offer no assurance that they will occur and be fully effective.

THE INSTITUTIONAL FRAMEWORK

The U. S. government has played a major role in the development of nuclear power, along with other nations. When those decisions become partisan, they can take a long time and change with the political party in power. Those difficulties were minimized as long as an AEC and a JCAE existed. Today, we have the independent NRC and the Department of Energy and their membership changes with the political party in charge. The best example of that difficult situation is the long time taken to resolve the problem of the disposal of spent fuel. After the abandonment of reprocessing and recycling, the U.S. government became responsible for spent fuel and selected deep underground geological repositories as the means of its disposal. The intent was to meet that obligation by 1988. While Congress and the president have finally agreed on using Yucca Mountain as the repository, it is not scheduled to receive spent fuel now until 2017—or about 30 years beyond the original date—and the two political parties are still not in full agreement about how the process will work. In retrospect, in a long cycle business such as nuclear power, it is important to have a stable institutional framework and that was far from being the case in 1977—and is still true today.

CONCLUSIONS

In 1977–1978, the development of nuclear power was in serious trouble because of the reduced need for energy, rising capital costs, increased duration of construction times, unpredictable regulatory assurance, doubts about plant safety, an unstable institutional framework, lack of comprehensive agreements about proliferation, and lack of an acceptable resolution regarding the disposal of spent fuel. Although progress has been made in all those issues, 28 years later some have still not been fully resolved.

SEVEN

THE CONSULTING YEARS

After leaving GE, I decided to let the available job market determine whether I should pursue teaching at a local university or become a consultant. In anticipation of consulting work, I leased space at the Pruneyard office building in Campbell, California. The building was within walking distance of my home. Henry Bose, a previous GE lawyer I knew, had an office in the same building and his advice was to incorporate to create a wall between the consulting business and the family possessions. S. Levy Incorporated (SLI) was formed and Henry Bose became its lawyer. Henry has served my commercial and personal needs extremely well while becoming a valued friend. Except for the GE consulting contract from Dr. Beaton, I did not seek more consulting work until I could find out whether Stanford or Berkeley were interested in having me join their faculty.

Stanford declined right away because they were in the process of dismantling their nuclear program and needed only young Ph.D. graduates. At Berkeley, C. L. Tien, a friend and an outstanding heat transfer engineer, was chairman of the Mechanical Engineering Department and he was interested in having me join the university. He indicated, however, that to hire me as a full professor, he would have to go through the process of advertising the position, interviewing applicants, and justifying my selection over other qualified candidates, and especially over minority and woman applicants. The process could take several months, so Tien suggested that I instead apply for an open assistant director position at the Lawrence Berkeley Laboratory (LBL) and that, if I was selected, he could arrange to have me teach in the engineering school and eventually get a full professorship.

The director of LBL was enthused about having me on his staff to run a newly formed Energy Development group. He also mentioned that there were other applicants and that the selection would rely heavily on the opinions of personnel in that group. I was asked to give a talk to my potential employees and to answer their questions and I agreed even though, considering my industrial background, I was surprised by the idea of employees selecting their boss rather than the other way around. The topic of my speech was "Some Lessons Learned from Nuclear Power Development." The speech pointed out that *foremost attention was put on the glamour side of the technology, i.e., the nuclear reactor, with not enough being done on the less attractive side. For example, closing of the fuel cycle, i.e., safeguarding of fissionable material, reprocessing, and high activity waste should have received much greater emphasis."* The LBL listeners had few questions and decided that my experience was overwhelmingly in nuclear power and selected a Ford Motor vice president for environmental programs. In retrospect, I should have spent possibly more time describing what I could do for LBL and not simply let my GE record, publications, and election to the Academy of Engineering in 1974 speak for themselves. It is also possible that, subconsciously, I tipped the scales toward becoming a consultant to the power industry because "I knew something about it." My consulting years will soon number 30 and I have no regret about the "special circumstances" that kept me away from academic life.

It did not take me very long to realize that a consultant can offer comments, suggestions, and recommendations but that the final decision rests with the line organization. I never told clients what they wanted to hear unless I believed in it. My consulting role was at its best when customers would take over a comment or suggestion, embellish the idea, and make it their own recommendation.

In the sections that follow, instead of describing my involvement in consulting work as a function of time, separate topical areas are covered to attain subject continuity. The following subjects are covered:

- Nuclear power plant review and oversight committees
- Advisory role during the Three Mile Island 2 (TMI-2) accident, Institute of Nuclear Operations (INPO) Advisory Council, the N Reactor, and Generation IV nuclear energy systems
- Participation in lawsuits
- Technical contributions.

NUCLEAR POWER REVIEW COMMITTEES

I have participated in a multitude of various reviews of nuclear power plants. The most important ones provided access to the board of directors and included the Duane Arnold plant of Iowa Electric, where I was a director; the Peach Bottom and Limerick plants of Philadelphia Electric Company, where I was a consultant to the board of directors; the Salem and Hope Creek plants of Public Service Electric and Gas; the Palo Verde plant of Arizona Public Service; the Pickering, Darlington, and Bruce plants of Ontario Power Generation in Canada, where I was a member of the Nuclear Oversight Committee; and the Oyster Creek plant of General Public Utilities Nuclear, where I served as a member of the General Office Review Board. My role at the Duane Arnold Energy Center will be described first because I could exert the most influence at that facility and it will be followed by my other appointments in the order listed above.

DUANE ARNOLD, IOWA

While at GE, I became acquainted with most of Iowa Electric's (IE's) top managers. I met the president of IE, Duane Arnold, during the final marketing presentation for a BWR to IE. After the sale was completed, I tended to give the nuclear plant named after the president a little extra attention because it was owned by a small utility that may have overreached beyond its means in purchasing a 581-MWe BWR. The GE project engineer for the IE plant was Larry Root and he worked in Design Engineering when I was its manager. Larry wanted to return to Iowa and decided to join IE where he progressed over the years to run their nuclear program and eventually to become president of the Energy Development and Nuclear Group of IES Utilities, Inc.

Chuck Sandford was put in charge of the Duane Arnold project and became IE executive vice president during the project's duration. Chuck did an outstanding job of putting together a group of young and very capable engineers to license and maintain the plant construction relatively on schedule. Chuck insisted on my presence at key ACRS, NRC, and final operation hearings. In spite of frequent and good humored teasing about my Jaguar car and its mechanical problems, we became friends and developed mutual respect for each other. Lee Liu, who had started in charge of engineering, with time became the executive vice president of IE and was chosen to be the president and chief executive officer of IE when Duane Arnold passed away. I had met Lee several times before his promotion to the presidency of IE.

Under those circumstances, it was not surprising that IE decided to hire me as a consultant after I resigned from GE. *The occasion was the discovery of stress corrosion cracking in the inlet water pipes to the reactor.* At that time, Chuck Sandford had left IE to become a Bechtel vice president and Sam Tuthill was the vice president in charge. Before leaving for Cedar Rapids, Iowa, I pointed out that there might be a conflict of interest due to my involvement in having directed the GE engineers responsible for that design, but both Sam and Lee did not consider it to be a problem. The cracks were the result of having a susceptible material (stainless steel), high stresses, and a concentration of impurities at a thermal sleeve that had been poorly designed. The decision was made to go with an improved reentry-type thermal sleeve design and to increase the pipe wall thickness to reduce the stresses. It was also suggested that management should have an independent review made of the plant water chemistry, which uncovered several deficiencies that had to be corrected. (Unfortunately, the same pipes cracked again many years later and were overlaid with weld metal because of poor welding practices during the first repair.)

My next assignment was to look at the squabbles between the plant manager and the "downtown" engineering function as well as NRC dissatisfaction with IE quality assurance. I prepared a management report which led to increasing the number of engineers at the site to perform the day-to-day engineering. Also, a new quality assurance manager was hired and Dick McCaughy, formerly with the U.S. Navy, was added to Tuthill's staff to help direct the nuclear program. I was asked to join the Safety Review Committee and I remained a member of that committee at the urging of Lee until the management of Duane Arnold was transferred to Nuclear Management Company.

Lee Liu often asked me to give him an outsider's perspective of problems and progress at Duane Arnold. Lee must have been satisfied because he appointed me a few years later to become a director of IE. The Safety Committee meetings were then scheduled on the afternoons of the day of the board meetings to reduce the number of trips I had to make from California. My assignment on the board was to explain to the other board members why it was necessary to make changes to Duane Arnold, to increase the number of employees, and to make additional capital investments. The other board members were lawyers, bankers, merchants, and retailers who were used to reducing costs. *The concept of excellence and the continued need to strive for it were foreign to the other board members* with the exception of Lee Liu who attended the yearly Institute for Nuclear Power Operations (INPO) Executive Conference. My presence on the board meant that Lee didn't have to justify the changes and increased costs while chairing the board meeting. Lee also assigned me to the compensation committee. Wayne Bevis, another ex-GE employee, was a member of the same committee. Both of us worked to raise the IE compensation methods to the enlightened levels prevailing in large industrial companies. Incentive and deferred compensation were introduced, and the awards were determined from specified performance goals. That strategy was also extended below the top management level with the nuclear managers being given special consideration because of the important role they had in avoiding safety risks at Duane Arnold.

During my years on the IE board, IE went through two mergers. The first one was with Iowa Southern to form IES, Inc., and the second merger was to form Alliant Energy with Wisconsin Public Service Corporation, part owner of the Kewaunee nuclear plant. After approval of the second merger, I did not stand for reelection to the board and Jack Newman, an excellent legal adviser to IE and the nuclear industry, was appointed to the board. Lee Liu, who remained chairman of the board, asked me to remain a board nuclear consultant and to work with Newman, the new chairman of the board's Environmental Subcommittee. Jack decided that a joint visit to Kewaunee might be appropriate.

For many years, Kewaunee had been a model plant with a high capacity factor and high ratings from both the NRC and INPO. However, *its steam generators needed to be replaced and, in order to buy new steam generators, the plant agreed to reduce its staffing level* (which was comparatively low) to compensate for the required large capital investment. *The cutback in engineering personnel increased the high backlog of design changes.* Also, the degree of quality assurance was minimal and there was no interest in self-assessment. One important advantage that Kewaunee had, however, was a very knowledgeable and experienced staff. They had worked together for many years effectively but *they did not see the need to change and to adopt the latest industry practices. They failed to realize that all the other plants were improving, which meant a decrease in Kewaunee ratings. Also, a mass exodus of experienced personnel was being predicted due to retirement and there was no plan to cope with it.*

> The cutback in engineering personnel increased the high backlog of design changes.

After that report reached the Alliant Energy board, I was asked to visit Kewaunee again with Elliot G. Protsch, the president of Alliant Energy at that time. A new plant manager had been appointed and additional engineers were added to reduce the engineering backlog, but I left unconvinced that a full cure was in place. Kewaunee was another nuclear plant assigned with Duane Arnold to Nuclear Management Company for operation. Most recently, Kewaunee was sold to Dominion Energy by its owners, Wisconsin Public Service and Wisconsin Power & Light. That sale was first rejected by the Wisconsin Public Service Commission because it would have taken the plant out of the rate base after 2013. The sale was subsequently accepted after proper modifications to the purchase agreement. I understand that the decision to sell Kewaunee by its owners may have been due to concerns about the plant performance, costs, and risks.

During my many years of consulting work at IE and other nuclear power plants, I became more and more convinced that *the most important variable influencing nuclear plant performance was top management attitude toward the plant and its safety. When plant costs and power production are put ahead of safety and effective performance, the plant rating is likely to deteriorate. It does not mean that plant costs are just allowed to grow. Instead, plant cost reductions are to be encouraged where they are justified because they improve management efficiency. (As a matter of fact, INPO has shown that the best performing plants were the least costly.)* Similarly, plant deficiencies need to be reported and corrected rather than being neglected to result in subsequent costly plant shutdowns. As shown in Figure 7.1 of the IES board, Lee Liu and Larry Root, the top two officers at IE and IES, Inc., understood those premises and my presence as an outsider on the board reinforced them. In my opinion, *having one or two recognized nuclear consultants on the board of companies owning nuclear power plants is essential to obtain an independent assessment of their nuclear program.* During my career, I had the opportunity to observe that *nuclear plants owned by boards with little nuclear power experience did not perform as well.*

Another conclusion formed at IE was the advisability of adding outsiders to the safety committees of nuclear power plants. Their presence can be beneficial because they bring to bear broad experience and because they can make comments that some employees will not offer in the presence of a supervisor or manager to whom they report. Two outside consultants with different fields of experience is recommended. I tended to handle the engineering function on most of my review committees. *My role consisted of making sure that the design basis was kept up to date, the root cause analyses were thorough, repeat events were avoided, engineers were trained appropriately and understood their equipment and systems, and that safety was first and foremost in all engineering decisions being made.* The duties assigned to the Safety Committee at Duane Arnold were extensive and required numerous meetings. I was allowed to have an alternate

> The most important variable influencing nuclear plant performance was top management attitude toward the plant and its safety.

when the Duane Arnold meetings conflicted with my other commitments. Dr. Harold Klepfer, who joined SLI after leaving GE, became my alternate in later years. Harold was such an effective replacement that his presence appeared to be favored over my more critical attitude. IE also, appointed a local university professor as their second outside member. When Dick McCaughy retired, he was also added to the membership of the Safety Committee.

In my last role as a consultant to the board, I reduced my visits to two times per year and spent the first day attending the morning meeting, visiting the plant, and talking to the vice president of Nuclear, the plant and outage managers, a few supervisors, and several employees. *I found the personnel interviews to be most useful in getting a quick assessment of the moral attitudes and physical conditions at the plant.* I attended the Safety Committee meeting during the second day. A report was issued to top management, who were kept aware of my scheduled visit to allow an exit meeting if so desired. I was also asked to conduct a special review of the training program because it did not pass the INPO assessment. To my great surprise, the Duane Arnold *training program had not kept up with the rest of the industry and there was inadequate ownership of training by the plant management.* The findings were taken seriously and as early indicators of a declining performance. Strong actions were taken to change training management and plant involvement. The great interest of Lee Liu and Larry Root in fixing the problem was a clear indication that top management's attitude toward Duane Arnold had not changed and that they would continue to strive for top performance.

Duane Arnold was a single unit of reduced power output. For that reason, its costs were high because they were applied to less generation of electricity and because some of the costs could not be shared with other units for such generic functions as engineering, plant security, quality assurance, training, and other areas. In other words, the single-plant conditions at Duane Arnold made it difficult to match the performance of multiple plants. Lee Liu and Larry Root, however, refused to give up on that objective and I encouraged them. The duration of refueling outages particularly needed to be reduced because plant capacity factor had a major role, as it should, in INPO evaluations. I urged visits to

Standing: David Q. Reed, C.R.S. Anderson, Blake O. Fisher, Jr., J. Wayne Bevis, Robert W. Schlutz
Seated: Dr. George Daly, Robert D. Ray, Lee Liu

ANNUAL MEETING

The annual meeting of the shareholders will be held at 2:00 p.m., Central Daylight Time on Tuesday, May 17, 1994 at the IE Tower, 6th floor, 200 First Street S.E. in Cedar Rapids, Iowa. A proxy statement with respect to this meeting will be mailed on or about April 4, 1994. All common shareholders are cordially invited to attend. However, those who are unable to attend in person are urged to promptly sign and return their proxy.

Standing: Larry D. Root, Henry Royer, G. Sharp Lannom, IV, René H. Malès
Seated: Robert F. Brewer, Dr. Salomon Levy, Anthony R. Weiler

BOARD OF DIRECTORS

C.R.S. Anderson (E) (A)
Retired Chairman of the Board of the Company

J. Wayne Bevis (A)
Vice Chairman & Chief Executive Officer, Pella Corporation (Window and Door Manufacturing), Pella, Iowa

Robert F. Brewer
Retired Chairman of the Board & Chief Executive Officer, Iowa Southern Utilities Company, Centerville, Iowa

Dr. George Daly (C)
Dean, Leonard Stern School of Business, New York University, New York, New York

Blake O. Fisher, Jr.
Executive Vice President & Chief Financial Officer of the Company

G. Sharp Lannom, IV (C)
President & Chief Executive Officer, DeLong Sportswear, Inc. (Sportswear Manufacturing), Grinnell, Iowa

Dr. Salomon Levy (C)
Chairman & Chief Executive Officer, S. Levy Incorporated (Engineering and Management Consulting), Campbell, California

Lee Liu (E) (N)
Chairman of the Board, President & Chief Executive Officer of the Company

René H. Malès
President and Group Executive, Generation and Engineering Group of IES Utilities Inc.

Robert D. Ray (A) (N)
President & Chief Executive Officer, Blue Cross and Blue Shield of Iowa (Insurance), Des Moines, Iowa

David Q. Reed (E)(N)
Attorney and Counselor at Law, Kansas City, Missouri

Larry D. Root
President and Group Executive, Energy Delivery and Nuclear Group of IES Utilities Inc.

Henry Royer (E) (C)
Chairman of the Board & President, Firstar Bank of Cedar Rapids, N.A., Cedar Rapids, Iowa

Robert W. Schlutz (A)
President, Schlutz Enterprises (Diversified Farming and Retailing), Columbus Junction, Iowa

Anthony R. Weiler (N)
Chairman & Chief Executive Officer, Chittenden & Eastman Company (Furniture Manufacturer and Distributor), Burlington, Iowa

DIRECTOR EMERITUS
Richard E. Scherling
Retired Merchant, Cedar Rapids, Iowa

(E) Member Executive Committee
(A) Member Audit Committee
(N) Member Nominating Committee
(C) Member Compensation Committee

Figure 7.1.   IES board of directors, 1994. (Source: IES Annual Report, 1994)

other foreign and U.S. BWRs where more planning and discipline were being used to shorten the outages. Those visits helped the Duane Arnold plant to achieve an equivalent result without being forced to fully adopt other plant approaches.

The staff at Duane Arnold has always worked as a cohesive team including the maintenance personnel even though that organization was unionized. I was told by the plant manager during one of my last visits that *the plant received an INPO 1 rating because the inspectors were very impressed by the enthusiasm and ownership of the plant shown by the maintenance personnel.* Another reason was the hiring of John Franz as the new vice president of Nuclear. I had met John at Peach Bottom when I became a consultant to the board of Philadelphia Electric Company. John knew BWR equipment well and how to keep it running safely. John was a perfect match for Duane Arnold because of his hands-on approach. He provided the right leadership to help Duane Arnold get an INPO 1 rating. John was a champion of self-assessment and he spent a lot of time at the plant reviewing equipment failures and using his extensive experience to help make the correct decisions. John also made it clear that he would not accept arbitrary cuts in budget and personnel but that he was willing to look for reductions. When both Kewaunee and Duane Arnold joined Nuclear Management Corporation, their costs of operation became available. The costs at Duane Arnold were higher than at Kewaunee but the difference, in my opinion, was more than justified by the enthusiasm and pride of Duane Arnold employees and the favorable inspection reports that the plant received.

My association with IE and IES, Inc., extended over about 25 years. It gave me exposure to the working of a utility board of directors and to a Duane Arnold staff willing to work hard and to improve. I was treated well by Lee Liu, Larry Root, Chuck Sandford, Sam Tuthill, Dick McCaughy, and John Franz who appreciated my involvement and accepted my advice judiciously.

NUCLEAR OVERSIGHT COMMITTEES

I have served on three nuclear oversight committees (NOCs), two in the United States and one in Canada. In another U.S. plant, I was an adviser to the Nuclear Subcommittee of the board. While the membership and structure vary from power company to company, the NOCs and the adviser role have several common characteristics:

- The nuclear power plants involved had a safety event or a performance degradation severe enough to justify the formation of NOCs.
- The U.S. plant conditions were serious enough to be investigated by an NRC special inspection team, which found many other plant inadequacies that had to be corrected;
- In all cases, the adverse conditions could not be reversed because the top management, at the time of their occurrence, minimized the problem's seriousness and had to be removed to be able to pursue a full root cause and a complete set of corrective actions.
- The NOCs reported to or had access to the board of directors of the owner/operator.

Before describing the conditions prevailing in each case, it should be noted that NOC members spend a limited amount of time at the plants because meetings are held periodically, bimonthly or quarterly, and scheduled ahead of time. Agendas are prepared, topics specified, and presenters identified. A summary presentation of key events since the last meeting by the site manager usually opens the meeting. Also, the NOCs determine the information they wish to receive between meetings and the degree to which they wish to be notified of important current events. A typical list would include regular inspections, monthly management reports, licensee event reports, audits and trending reports, and INPO evaluations.

NUCLEAR OVERSIGHT COMMITTEE
AT SALEM-HOPE CREEK, NEW JERSEY

A failure to scram event occurred at the Salem nuclear plant. It was a very important event because the means to shut down the power plant were lost. It led to the formation of an NOC in which all members of the NOC were outsiders. In March 1991, the membership of the NOC consisted of Dr. Melvin Gottlieb, in charge of the fusion program at

Princeton; Dr. Shirley Jackson, from AT&T Laboratories and a director of Public Service Electric and Gas (PSE&G); J. Phillip Bayne, president of the U.S. Council for Energy Awareness and formerly in charge of the James A. Fitzpatrick BWR in New York State; and Henry Hukill, formerly plant manager of Three Mile Island 1 (TMI-1), who had replaced Dennis Wilkinson, the first president of INPO. (Membership of NOCs changes over time as members resign or new members are appointed by top management).

There are two PWR units at the Salem site, producing 1096 and 1092 MWe. Also, a BWR plant, named Hope Creek, had restarted construction after a long delay and it would produce 1049 MWe during the tenure of the NOC. The Salem plant's performance was average or slightly below average before the failure to scram and they moved to the "troubled" plant category after the failure to scram. In the United States, once a plant gets assigned to that class of reactors, it is expected to remain shut down for about one year while the equipment and documentation are improved in accordance with a plan approved by the NRC.

The PSE&G chief nuclear officer, Dick Eckert, had considerable nuclear experience and he was a great supporter of nuclear power. For example, he was the principal proponent of barge-mounted nuclear plants to standardize them and to reduce their construction time. *Like most officers of other troubled plants, he felt that Salem was being picked on and that the corrective program was excessive.* That perspective has a tendency to increase costs and duration of the recovery program and to have the NOC encourage a change in management to be able to pursue a complete root cause and to instill an improved performance and safety attitude.

When the NOC first arrived at the site, *there were many equipment problems that kept the plants from producing electricity.* For example, the circulating water system had many piping and heat exchanger failures due to very poor water chemistry, and the pumps were unable to produce the required flows especially when grass was present in the water. Also, the plant documentation needed upgrading, and most of all, maintenance production was low and could not keep up with needed repairs. One of the problems with the engineering staff was that many of the original designers refused to transfer to the site from Newark. A comprehensive engineering work list was not available and schedules were not being met. The plants continued to have *several unanticipated shutdowns,* which I kept referring to *as "talk" by the Salem plants to their operating and support staff to correct equipment problems before they led to forced plant outages. Those failures eventually led to PSE&G top management agreeing to make a change in their top nuclear management.* Corbin McNeill was hired to run PSE&G's nuclear program. At that time

> **Those failures eventually led to PSE&G top management agreeing to make a change in their top nuclear management.**

Corbin was in charge of the Fitzpatrick plant. I was also given the opportunity to discuss the engineering situation with the board of directors. A few months later, Tom Crimmins was appointed engineering vice president. I had worked with Tom before when he was in charge of Oyster Creek engineering and I was very enthused about his selection.

Corbin McNeill was a strong leader and a great motivator. He redefined the corrective action plan and met the revised schedules. He would visit the plant at all hours of the day and night and would talk to everybody he met. He spent time with maintenance personnel to increase their productivity and he did not hesitate to make personnel changes when necessary. He listened to suggestions and let you know if he agreed or disagreed with them. For example, he allowed the installation of a service water test loop with different material sections to determine the various materials' resistance to stress corrosion attack under actual river plant conditions. Corbin also vigorously pursued the completion of Hope Creek and its NRC license for operation. In order to spend more time at headquarters, Corbin interviewed several candidates and selected the plant manager at Callaway, which was an INPO 1 plant, to run the Salem site. Similarly, Tom Crimmins developed goals and a full schedule for engineering work. The attitude and production in engineering improved fast. During that transition, the president of PSE&G retired and Jim Ferland, who had considerable nuclear experience at NorthEast Utilities, was chosen to replace him, which pleased the NOC.

The Salem recovery program was near completion when Corbin McNeill was allowed to transfer to Philadelphia Electric Company

(PECO) to handle the troubled Peach Bottom plants. That decision had considerable merit because PSE&G and PECO were co-owners of both Salem and Peach Bottom plants. Tom Crimmins was also selected for a promotion to a position at headquarters. His chosen successor, however, had difficulties managing the engineering function and resigned. After those departures, the Salem plant performance began to deteriorate and, eventually, an event occurred in which the operators decided to add reactivity to raise power to avoid a plant shutdown. The NOC felt that the action was a serious error in judgment that the site management should have pursued more aggressively. A meeting was requested and held with Jim Ferland to relay the NOC concern about the reactivity event. Ferland listened and made changes in management. Also, he formed a new NOC and replaced the two most vocal members. As far as I was concerned, this was an appropriate change due to my long tenure.

> A strong leader and a great motivator at the top of a nuclear program can make a great difference in the safety and operational effectiveness of nuclear power plants.

Based on this first experience with an NOC, it is believed that:

- When a nuclear power plant has a serious event such as a failure to scram, an NOC can provide the board of directors with a different perspective on the situation, especially if the embattled management is reluctant to accept the need for significant changes.
- As demonstrated at Salem, *a strong leader and a great motivator at the top of a nuclear program can make a great difference in the safety and operational effectiveness of nuclear power plants.* The same is true for a good engineering manager.
- The safety consciousness of Salem personnel was never in question. The issues were more "in the practices moulding the environment and fostering attitudes conducive to safety." As noted in the IAEA's *Characteristics of a Good Safety Culture* (INSAG-12), which is reproduced in Chapter 9 as Table 9.1, "it is the responsibility of managers to institute such practices in accordance with their organization safety policy and objectives."

- The tenure of NOC members should be limited. A good time to terminate the Salem-Hope Creek NOC would have been after changes were made at the president, top nuclear officer, and engineering manager levels, and after good performance progress was noted. Beyond that point, it is preferable to return the responsibility for management to the line functions.

While writing this section, I could not help but notice that the NRC had just decided to increase its scrutiny at Salem-Hope Creek. NRC has "concluded that there were numerous indications of weaknesses in corrective actions and management efforts to establish an environment where employees are consistently willing to raise safety concerns. Some PSE&G staff and managers felt that the company had emphasized production to a point that negatively impacted handling of emergent equipment issues and associated operational decision making. Additionally *management had not been supportive of station staff identifying concerns and providing alternate views* (*Nuclear News,* October 2004). Call it safety-conscious work environment (SCWE) or safety culture, they are similar. The term *safety culture* was first introduced in the review of the Chernobyl Accident (INSAG-1). It was further expanded in INSAG-3, *Basic Safety Principles for Nuclear Plants,* and it was refined in INSAG-4, *Safety Culture.* INSAG-12 defines the characteristics of a good safety culture, and INSAG-15 covers their application to the management of operational safety in nuclear power plants. The term *safety culture* is being used increasingly in connection with international nuclear plant safety and it *deserves increased consideration in the United States.* Most recently, Exelon and PSE&G have agreed to merge and Exelon has taken over the operation of PSE&G's power reactors before the merger is complete to help resolve "the recurring management and operational problems at Salem-Hope Creek."

I have fond memories of the Salem/Hope Creek NOC and the PSE&G employees I had the opportunity to meet. In particular, it gave me the chance to work with such very talented NOC members as Phil Bayne, Mel Gottlieb, Henry Hukill, Shirley Jackson, and Dennis Wilkinson. I was impressed by Shirley Jackson's fast pickup of nuclear power specifics and her chairing of the NOC. Also, I developed a friendly and respectful relationship with Dennis Wilkinson, which carried over to several other power plants.

PEACH BOTTOM, PENNSYLVANIA

At Peach Bottom, *operators were sleeping while the power plant was running.* This is a very serious event because the operators are expected to notice adverse plant conditions and to correct them. The president of Philadelphia Electric Company (PECO) immediately called Dennis Wilkinson, the first and former president of INPO, and asked him to become a consultant to the PECO board of directors. Dennis agreed to help if he could be joined by a second consultant knowledgeable about BWRs and he suggested my name. I knew most of the top PECO nuclear personnel well because I had been the manager of Design Engineering for GE when Peach Bottom was being licensed and constructed. As a matter of fact, I went to the last Peach Bottom ACRS meeting with the president of PECO, James L. Everett, who was the chief nuclear officer at that time. I agreed to work with Dennis after a short phone call from the PECO president. In contrast to other nuclear power producers, PECO was an early entry in that field. It had built and successfully operated the Peach Bottom 1 plant, a 40-MWe high-temperature gas reactor (HTGR), since June 1967. PECO was familiar with the special safety demands of nuclear power generation and relied on the internal growth of its staff and management to handle the two BWR Peach Bottom Units 2 and 3, the Limerick-1 BWR, and the Limerick-2 unit, which had been delayed and was being completed.

The first meeting Dennis and I attended was the presentation of the root cause analysis and proposed corrective action program to return the Peach Bottom units to power. Members from INPO were present as well as staff from Management Analysis Company (MAC) who had helped draft the material. The general consensus at the meeting was that the root cause analysis was quite narrow and the program quite limited in its scope. A revised write-up was to be prepared and the board consultants were to get a copy. There was a major snowfall that evening in Philadelphia and all the flights to California were canceled. The INPO personnel had gone to the airport hoping to board a flight to Atlanta but they came back to our hotel and joined us for dinner. The INPO personnel pointed out that they had met the top nuclear PECO managers at the airport and that those managers believed that the Peach Bottom issue was limited to a few operators. The INPO personnel planned to recount that encounter to Zack Pate, the president of INPO, who was very disappointed with the inadequate response of the top PECO managers prior to and after the sleeping episode.

PECO did not have an NOC. Instead, *a Nuclear Committee of the Board (NCB) was formed and it used two consultants for advice.* The two consultants received specified written material and they then prepared short letters summarizing their opinions and findings to the NCB ahead of the board meeting. The consistency between the two consultants' letters was quite remarkable. The NCB had five members. Initially, Bob Harrison was the chairman of the NCB and he had an uncanny ability to reach an NCB consensus and to express it. John Palms took over in later years. He was then the president of the University of South Carolina and did not need to be sensitized to the need for training. The other board members included Edith J. Levit, an M.D. who had been in charge of the licensing of doctors in the state of Pennsylvania; Admiral Kinnard R. McKee, who ran the Naval Reactor Branch and had been in charge of the Naval Academy before retiring from the U.S. Navy; and Joseph J. McLaughlin, a local banker who was fascinated by the subject matter and focused on financial issues. Figure 7.2 shows Peach Bottom's Nuclear Committee of the Board on June 13, 1989.

The day before board meetings, the consultants would visit the plants or the central Support Division location to listen to presentations and talk to PECO personnel and sometimes NRC resident inspectors to form additional opinions. The following day, the consultants attended the portion of the board meeting dealing with nuclear matters. While waiting to be called in, the consultants would agree on the items to be covered and which consultant would cover what topic. During the board meeting, top nuclear management went first and summarized the plants status, key issues, and the plans to address them. Dennis Wilkinson went

Peach Bottom Atomic Power Station
Nuclear Committee
of the Board
June 13, 1989

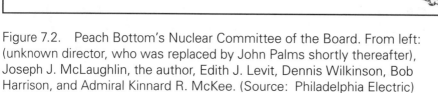

Figure 7.2.   Peach Bottom's Nuclear Committee of the Board. From left:
(unknown director, who was replaced by John Palms shortly thereafter),
Joseph J. McLaughlin, the author, Edith J. Levit, Dennis Wilkinson, Bob
Harrison, and Admiral Kinnard R. McKee. (Source: Philadelphia Electric)

next because of his more deliberate and effective presentation. Dennis also took the time to write down his comments and make them available to the board secretary. My comments were last and tended to be more regulatory and engineering oriented. Dennis and I were able to participate in each other's talk without disturbing the flow of information. When our presentations were finished, we were driven to the airport to catch flights to California.

After the unsatisfactory meeting on the root cause and corrective action program for the Peach Bottom incident, the consultants became much more aware of Zack Pate's concerns about the inadequate PECO management response. INPO had gone back and reviewed Peach Bottom past performance evaluations and found *several precursors that management had overlooked and not taken seriously enough.* It was clear that Pate felt that *PECO top management was not taking sufficient responsibility for their role in the latest crisis.* By that time, the root cause and the corrective action programs had been expanded considerably to become acceptable. Agreement to proceed was still lacking between INPO and PECO in spite of a flurry of telephone calls between their top officers. Face-to-face meetings, for instance, one between Bob Harrison, chairman of the NCB, and Zack Pate, were not successful. INPO finally decided to issue a very strong letter recounting past and current failures by PECO to take appropriate action and make it available to the NRC chairman, and therefore to the media. When the INPO letter was published, it had a great impact on PECO and its top-level officers.

Major changes followed at PECO. The top two officers left and a new president, Joe Paquette, was appointed. Joe was an excellent choice because he had worked at PECO before leaving to join Consumers Power Company. His relationship with employees was very good and he took the time to visit the nuclear plants frequently and to boost the morale of the workers. He was able to negotiate the move of Corbin McNeill from PSE&G to PECO. (When asked for candidates for chief nuclear officer, Dennis and I listed Corbin as the number one as well as the number two choice.) The previous chief nuclear officer agreed to report to Corbin and he was assigned to complete the construction and startup of Limerick-2. That task was carried out extremely well by meeting cost and schedule targets and by insisting that Unit 2 be a full duplicate of Unit 1. I still remember the general agreement that "*it is too bad that we quit building nuclear power plants when we finally learned how to do it.*"

"It is too bad that we quit building nuclear power plants when we finally learned how to do it."

The biggest issue facing PECO was that of having enough operators to restart Peach Bottom after intensive interviews reduced their available number. The additional operators found were barely enough meet crew requirements. A new operations manual was generated that emphasized the overriding safety responsibility of the operators. During the interviews, it was found that *the operators felt that they had no growth opportunity, that they were not allowed to transfer to the new Limerick plants,* and that the material conditions at Peach Bottom were being allowed to deteriorate. Actions were taken in all complaint areas and included arrangements with a local college for additional education, promotions of operators to quality assurance and other positions, and a major material improvement program. A new apprentice program was also implemented.

Dickinson Smith, a former naval officer recommended by Wilkinson, was appointed vice president for Peach Bottom. He took full charge of the improvement program. He was not as fast as Corbin, but was just as effective. The operator training pipeline had been allowed to dry up and a new class was initiated. The operators were retrained with the new operations manual. Those training sessions were attended by the top managers, PECO officers, and INPO and NRC personnel. Most valves were opened up and refurbished. The primary recirculation water piping was replaced to avoid stress corrosion cracking. Equipment identification was improved, and several floors and walls were painted.

There was no question that PECO was eager to return Peach Bottom to a high performance level. They used many INPO assistance visits to identify problem areas and correct them. They performed yearly self-assessments, sometimes actually waiting only six months between assessments, if necessary. A Nuclear Review Board with outside members was formed and it met about every month. They had an Independent Safety Engineering Group (ISEG) at each station. *ISEG evaluations were outstanding and did not hesitate to blame management when the blame belonged there.* Initially, the number of discovered problems exceeded the number that could be corrected at once, so prioritization and performance indicators were used to work on the most important items.

Eventually, Peach Bottom was ready for restart and Corbin McNeill invited Dennis and myself to sit and comment on a Readiness Review meeting, which we did. When the plant was allowed to restart, the consultants received a letter of gratitude from Bob Harrison, reproduced in Figure 7.3, which attests to our perceived contributions.

After the plant returned to power, there were a few setbacks, as expected. The biggest surprise was the INPO evaluation of 1993, which identified 17 findings. After recovering from the shock, PECO management put together a step-up plan to correct the situation. *The plan required management and supervisors to assume the responsibilities of communicating, coaching, and reinforcing their expectations about how to operate Peach Bottom to all employees and to hold those employees accountable for their own words, actions, and deeds.* Definite progress needed to be made within six months because Corbin was able to get INPO to agree to another assessment at that time.

Many of the INPO criticisms were valid and included insufficient monitoring and coaching of workers, supervisors not providing enough oversight and coaching to reinforce expectations, continued plant transients and equipment malfunctions, insufficient engineering activities to resolve plant problems, and inadequate modification installation, testing, and closeout. In my opinion, it is likely that INPO did not want Peach Bottom management to get an overblown opinion of their progress. *It was also a reminder that nuclear power plants require continued improvement and vigilance as well as an*

ROBERT D. HARRISON
The Fidelity Court Building
259 Radnor-Chester Road
Suite 220
Radnor, Pennsylvania   19087
(215) 293-0210

May 9, 1989

Dr. Solomon Levy, President
S. LEVY, INC.
3425 South Basion Avenue
Campbell, CA 95008

Dear Sal:

The news of the end and the beginning in April 29, was welcome indeed.

Your assistance, experience and wisdom have contributed significantly to the pleasures we are currently enjoying. We need you and appreciate your insight and dedication to our effort.

On behalf of the Committee, the management and particularly, myself, thank you. Still a long road and we need you.

Sincerely,

Robert D. Harrison

RDH/bjf

Figure 7.3.   Letter of gratitude for work done to get the Peach Bottom plant back on line. (Source: Robert D. Harrison, 1989)

all-pervading safety strategy. Six months went by and the second INPO assessment showed considerable improvement.

It is typical of troubled plants to hire additional personnel and increase their capital costs while implementing a recovery plan. Peach Bottom was in that category and the time arrived to reduce the budget. *Instead of an arbitrary decrease, Dickinson Smith reopened all positions and starting from the top appointed the best person for each position.* When the current holder of a position did not retain that current status, he or she was given the opportunity to look at other positions available with the company, take an early retirement, or accept a reduced role. In this case, the strategy worked because the promotions were deserved and overdue and the overall result was to improve morale rather than hurt it. The consultants were given a chance to review the plan and provided a joint comment letter. The consultants supported the cost reduction program, encouraged fast completion of the reorganization, and suggested less reduction of independent safety assessment groups.

Peach Bottom continued to improve and eventually got a well-deserved INPO 1 rating. The role of the consultants consisted of prodding management along that improvement road.

The consultants were also asked to monitor the performance of the Limerick units, which were in much better shape physically and operationally. On completion of the construction of Limerick-2, it successfully reached full power. Corbin McNeill then decided to increase the energy level at that site and appointed Dave R. Helwig, director of engineering, as vice president, Limerick. That promotion left an important void in the engineering organization and a former employee of Bechtel was hired to replace Dave. The NCB was encouraged by the consultants to have the new director of engineering present his plans when they were ready. At a meeting held in Washington, D.C., the engineering organization and plans were discussed in detail. Because the goals appeared to be overly ambitious, a follow-up meeting was scheduled. Very little progress had been made by the second meeting, possibly due to the lack of support by the supervisors and lead engineers for an outsider. It was impressive to see the NCB members decry the lack of progress without the help of the consultants. John Cotton, director of Nuclear Quality Assurance, agreed to take over engineering and did *a remarkably good job of prioritizing the work and restoring responsibility and commitment for the work output.*

In the meantime, Dave Helwig energized the entire Limerick organization. Dave was very smart and an excellent motivator. He had every supervisor develop performance goals and meet or exceed them. The enthusiasm at Limerick was high with Dave broadcasting the accomplishments as they were satisfied. If Dave had a shortcoming, it may have been giving insufficient credit to the supervisors/persons responsible for some of the progress. One key result of the reorganization was that Limerick was the first BWR plant to complete a refueling outage in the record time of about 20 days. Also, the maintenance backlog was kept to a minimum by doing online maintenance. It did not take very long for Limerick to receive an INPO 1 rating and to set the standard that Peach Bottom had to meet.

That does not mean that Limerick performance was problem free. In 1988 a water chemistry intrusion led to several fuel failures due to crud-induced localized corrosion (CILC) at Limerick-1. The failures were due to a large intrusion (700 gallons) of fluid from the electro-hydraulic control (EHC) system of the steam turbine generator. The failed fuel rods exhibited extensive regions of heavy deposits of iron and especially copper oxides, which are known to cause localized accelerated fuel failures. A team of experts was assembled to develop potential options to resolve the problem. The ultimate choice was to reduce the input of iron and copper oxides into the reactor by installing both a deep bed and a filter demineralizer water cleanup system. (*Most other BWRs solved the problem by eliminating the presence of copper by instead using titanium condenser tubes.* That option was not available at Limerick because its design did not provide for an easy replacement of those tubes.) Other changes were made to the EHC system and the fuel cladding material to help eliminate CILC at Limerick.

In September 1995, Limerick-1 had another serious problem that impacted Peach Bottom and Limerick. The immediate response of PECO provided another indication of PECO dedication to excellence. There was an inadvertent opening of a relief valve in the Limerick suppression pool. The steam release stirred the pool sludge consisting primarily of iron oxide particulates, which were drawn into the two residual heat removal (RHR) suction strainers along with some "latent" fiber material present in the pool. One RHR pump cavitated and the other pump suffered a major loss in its net positive suction head (NPSH). This event led immediately to periodic cleaning of BWR suppression pools (about

635 pounds of debris were removed from Limerick-1 and a comparable amount from unit 2).

The pump event also reopened the issue of sump clogging in BWRs. A short and good history of that problem is provided by G. H. Hart in the March 2004 issue of *Nuclear News*. The history shows that originally blockage of sump screens and suction strainers was presumed to be only a fibrous insulation issue and that 50 percent blockage of the flow areas was judged to be conservative enough to allow core and containment cooling to proceed. In summer 1992, there was a strainer blockage at the Barseback plant in Sweden, and in springs 1992 and 1993, there were strainer blockages and a sharp drop in the RHR pump NPSH at the Perry BWR power plant in North Perry, Ohio. Those events showed that the filtration of corrosion product dust and other debris by a thin layer of fibrous material could result in a very high head loss and that this head loss was not linear with respect to the amount of fibers present; that is, 1 cubic foot of fibers could produce a higher head loss than 100 cubic feet of fibers. The Limerick-1 event confirmed those results.

The solution to the plugging of sumps and strainers was complicated by the inability to identify the source and quantity of "latent" fibers, the composition of the sludge material, the different strainer designs in BWRs, and the three different pressure suppression containment configurations. Those uncertainties led to an "overkill" to resolve the problem by using very large surface area passive strainers because the head loss across them was inversely proportional to the strainer surface area raised to a power of 2.5.

The installed screens are illustrated in Figure 7.4 for the Peach Bottom plant, which employs an inverted light bulb pressure suppression configuration like that shown in Figure 4.2. The backfit costs for enlarged areas ranged from $2 to $4 million. *The suction strainer problem at Limerick was detailed because it was identified as early as the late 1970s and its first resolution was based on wrong assumptions. It took close to 30 years and three plugging incidents in actual BWRs to resolve it and to recognize the need to solve the issue with margins because of the uncertainties involved. Ex-reactor prototypic tests with a variety of blockage constituents would have led to a much earlier and less costly solution.* It is interesting to note that

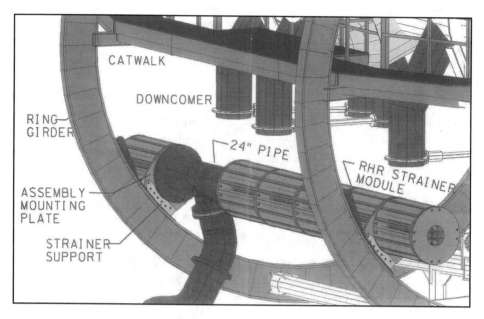

Figure 7.4.   Peach Bottom large surface area passive strainers.
(Source: Philadelphia Electric)

Keeping an INPO 1 rating may be more difficult than getting it.

belatedly PWRs faced a similar problem in their sump design in 2004.

After PECO received an INPO 1 rating for Peach Bottom and Limerick, the nuclear officers became much more confident (as they should have), such that they could manage their nuclear plants with less prodding from consultants. Dennis Wilkinson was the first to leave because his hearing, damaged by large navy guns during World War II, deteriorated to the point that he had trouble following conversations at board meetings. He was replaced by H. Hukill who left due to bad health, and then it was time for the most critical consultant to resign and I did. At my going away dinner, I closed with the statement that *keeping an INPO 1 rating may be more difficult than getting it.*

Based on the experience with an NCB, it is believed that:

- An NCB is superior to an NOC because it has to be staffed by some board members with nuclear experience and because the role of outside experts is limited to consulting rather than over-sight.

- INPO rather than consultants should encourage top nuclear management change when it is necessary. INPO may find it difficult to do because those same managers may sit on the board of directors of INPO. Bob Harrison's guidance was exceptional during this very difficult period of time at PECO.
- Top management leadership is essential to the safe and efficient performance of nuclear power plants.
- Unexpected failures such as the fuel damage and plugging of strainers at Limerick can provide a valuable assessment of management's safety attitude because such problems must be solved fast and correctly.

As a consultant to the PECO NCB, I especially enjoyed working with Dennis Wilkinson because of his full understanding of the operating side of the business and because he had an uncanny ability to interview personnel and to make them feel at ease. We formed a compatible team that was listened to at all levels of the organization and particularly by NCB members, Joe Paquette, and the top PECO nuclear officers.

NUCLEAR OVERSIGHT COMMITTEE AT PALO VERDE, ARIZONA

The serious event at Palo Verde was the rupture of a steam generator tube that tripped all three units, which were generating close to 4000 MWe. The detection of the rupture and the response to it were inadequate and required the implementation of a corrective action plan to be approved by the NRC. The operating company and part owner of Palo Verde, Arizona Public Service (APS), decided to form an NOC, I suspect, at the urging of Dennis Wilkinson. The NOC membership included Dennis, Bob Matlock, a consulting engineer, Don C. Hintz, who became the president of Entergy Operations, the author, and a retiree of APS who had an early and important role during the initial phase of purchasing and construction of Palo Verde.

Initially, the NOC met with the board of directors of APS, at which time the NOC members, particularly Dennis, explained that the return of Palo Verde to power would take a long period of time and considerable resources. The NOC also met with the young manager who was seen to have a highly promising future. He was put in charge of the recovery at Palo Verde. Like all members of the board, he did not have any experience with nuclear power and he made noises about arguing with NRC and INPO to reduce and accelerate the corrective action plan. Shortly thereafter, he left that position for personal reasons.

At the following meeting, the NOC members had received ahead of time a copy of the NRC safety assessment of the Palo Verde site and they tried to discuss issues being raised by the NRC with the Palo Verde management. Surprise! The NRC report had not been read by the site manager or any of the three plant managers. At the exit interview with the president of APS, the NOC members pointed out how that was unacceptable and I still remember Don Hintz stating that, at his plant, all the managers would read the report immediately and then meet to decide how to resolve all of the NRC issues in the report.

The result of that surprise was a search for a new chief nuclear officer with a lot of nuclear experience who was rated highly by INPO. Bill Conway was hired. I had met Bill earlier when he was in charge of the Vermont Yankee BWR and I was the general manager of GE's Fuel Department. Bill Conway was a good choice. He first established a good relationship with the local NRC regional manager, Jack Martin, and made sure he kept him well informed about problems at the site. Systematically, all the managers reporting to him were changed. For example, he brought in Jim Levine from Arkansas Nuclear Power to take over operations, Gregg Overbeck from Detroit Edison to run Systems Engineering, Dave Mauldin to run Palo Verde outages, Jack Bailey to run Licensing, a new director of engineering, a new QA manager, and so on. He was able to get the board of directors to agree to the funding of administrative buildings at the Palo Verde site and to the ordering of two plant simulators to train the operators. The impact was a major boost in site morale. It also allowed the relocation of the engineering function from downtown Phoenix to complete the *long overdue completion of the transition of Palo Verde from engineering to operations.*

As a member of the NOC, I tried to highlight long-term, high-risk equipment issues to make sure that the board of directors and the president became aware of them. At the top of the list was the anticipated need to deal with steam generator corrosion, tube plugging, and steam generator replacement. These issues were followed by the deteriorating cooling tower material condition and its influence on the working environment; next, came the integrity of the underground piping that delivered sewage treated water to the site for heat rejection.

During that time, the NOC provided its best advice on organization, personnel, managers, NRC concerns, and morale attitude. The recovery action plan was defined, approved, and progressed satisfactorily to allow the units to return to power. Also, with the approval of Bill Conway, I was asked to chair the Engineering Subcommittee of the Offsite Safety Review Committee (OSRC). I did not feel comfortable being a member of both the NOC and OSRC because I would have to sit on some topics twice and because it restricted the other NOC members from pursuing engineering topics as deeply as they wished.

With time, all the NOC members noticed a growing tension between Bill Conway and the APS president and decided to send their most politically astute member, Dennis Wilkinson, to improve that relationship. Conditions got better but not for long because Bill Conway decided to leave APS and retire. I suspect that Bill Conway was unhappy with his advancement in the company and that he had difficulties working with a president and board members who didn't have hands-on nuclear experience.

The NOC advice to the APS president was again to get another chief nuclear officer recommended by INPO and with proven experience. Bill Stewart, who was in charge of Virginia Electric Power Company's nuclear plants, now referred to as Dominion Energy, was hired. Shortly thereafter, I resigned from the NOC to avoid being on two APS committees. Dennis was also able to have APS add to their board Ken Carr, former chairman of the NRC, as a director. Subsequently, Dennis arranged for Bob Matlock, chairman of the NOC, to receive a well-deserved promotion to the board of APS.

Once again, *the NOC accomplished its mission to make the APS board of directors understand the difficult recovery program they were facing, get the best available nuclear officer to take charge of Palo Verde, and eventually obtain an INPO 1 rating.* The NOC and Dennis Wilkinson were also able to add directors to the board who had strong nuclear backgrounds. Stewart took over a well-staffed organization and first-class facilities. He implemented his approach of identifying the top 10 issues and holding regular meetings with his first- and second-level managers to discuss resolution of those issues and their assignment, schedule, and progress. For example, a new water chemistry group was formed to improve water chemistry conditions on the secondary side of Palo Verde's steam generators. As issues on the top 10 list were resolved, others were added. Stewart's presence was being felt much more by the employees and, particularly, *in the control room where he introduced a new culture and behavior.*

> Responsibility, schedule, and funding were established for each issue and progress was reported regularly.

I was most influential when Bill Ide became the vice president of engineering because he was responsive to my comments. He had that unique ability to take suggestions and to improve on them. For example, he assembled a book describing the key engineering issues and the programs to resolve them. *Responsibility, schedule, and funding were established for each issue and progress was reported regularly.* Ide also issued a set of engineering principles and expectations. He kept a list of backup managers for his organization and he would talk to his engineers. (Engineers appreciate attention and favorable comments!) Bill was tough when necessary and did not hesitate to move nonperforming supervisors and engineers. I always knew when he did not like my ideas. I was sorry to see him take an early retirement—the plants' performance reflected his departure.

On December 9, 2004, I participated in my last Palo Verde OSRC meeting as a member of the Engineering Subcommittee. The organization of the Palo Verde OSRC in July 1992 is reproduced in Figure 7.5 because it is, in my opinion, one of the better ones and Jack Bailey and Bill Conway deserve the credit for it. It was chaired by K. W. Hamlin, the nuclear safety director, an employee on loan from INPO. It consisted of five subcommittees, headed by outsiders. Each of the outsiders was supported by two Palo Verde employees to help investigate potential safety issues and to arrange for discussion and presentations on those issues. The OSRC functions were then written into the licensing documents, and the NRC reviewed the committee's reports to make sure that the important safety events were being handled correctly. The OSRC held periodic meetings of one day's duration and made recommendations to Palo Verde management.

The caliber of the outside members listed in Figure 7.5 is especially noteworthy. It included such talent as J. D. Schiffer, senior vice president of Pacific Gas & Electric (PG&E); J. G. Keppler, formerly the NRC midwest regional director; C. K. Seaman, assistant plant manager at the Trojan nuclear plant, who later took over Nuclear Assurance at Palo Verde; and T. A. Peterson, an outstanding radiological expert. It was a pleasure to listen to the opinions and comments from all that talent.

Before I left, the OSRC was being run by Dave Mauldin, engineering vice president, and it had two subcommittees. Each subcommittee has two outside members. For example the Engineering and Maintenance Subcommittee has L. F. Womack, vice president, PG&E, as a member in addition to me while Operations and Plant Support has G. E. Kane, consultant, and R. Ridenoure from Calhoun Nuclear Power as members. *The addition of members from other plants is a good idea* because it reduces costs by exchanging members between power plants and it gives Palo Verde officers an opportunity to participate in other plants' safety review committees.

Periodic OSRC meetings are still held but less often, and last for two days. The first day is spent looking at mostly topics assigned by the chairman. The second day involves listening to the plant operational history, topical subjects of interest, and plant review board, licensing, and nuclear assurance status summaries followed by subcommittee reports. At the end of the meeting the chair would list key findings and recommendations to be covered with top management.

The OSRC still had to approve changes in technical specifications, but the committee's contributions to plant safety became limited because of its reduced participation in solving safety issues such as vibra-

DIRECTORY
OFFSITE SAFETY REVIEW COMMITTEE
SUBCOMMITTEES

OSRC CHAIRMAN

K. W. Hamlin, Director
Nuclear Safety Division
ARIZONA PUBLIC SERVICE
PVNGS
Station 1536
P. O. Box 52034
Phoenix, Arizona 85072-2034
(602) 340-4201
FAX: (602) 250-4989 – Box 5D

T. E. Matlock, Manager
Nuclear Safety Department
ARIZONA PUBLIC SERVICE
PVNGS
Station 1536
P. O. Box 52034
Phoenix, Arizona 85072-2034
(602) 340-4133
FAX: (602) 250-4989 -- Box 5D

LICENSING

J. G. Keppler
Nuclear Management Consultant
324 South Park Boulevard
Glen Ellyn, Illinois 60132
(708) 858-7226
FAX: (708) 858-9010

J. S. Taggart
ARIZONA PUBLIC SERVICE
PVNGS
Station 7616
P. O. Box 52034
Phoenix, Arizona 85072-2034
(602) 393-5192
FAX: (602) 393-5285 -- Box 20

R. W. Riedel
ARIZONA PUBLIC SERVICE
PVNGS
Station 7198
P. O. Box 52034
Phoenix, Arizona 85072-2034
(602) 393-1088

OPERATIONS

James D. Shiffer
Sr. V.P./General Manager
PACIFIC GAS & ELECTRIC
Room 1451
77 Beale
San Francisco, California 94106
(415) 973-7540

D. G. Marks
ARIZONA PUBLIC SERVICE
PVNGS
Station 1536
P. O. Box 52034
Phoenix, Arizona 85072-2034
(602) 340-4150
FAX: (602) 250-4989 -- Box 5D

P. L. Brandjes
ARIZONA PUBLIC SERVICE
PVNGS
Station 1536
P. O. Box 52034
Phoenix, Arizona 85072-2034
(602) 340-4201
FAX: (602) 250-4989 -- Box 5D

QUALITY

C. K. Seaman
Assistant Plant General Manager,
TROJAN
71760 Columbia River Highway
Rainier, Oregon 97048
(503) 556-6482

R. E. Gouge
ARIZONA PUBLIC SERVICE
PVNGS
Station 7610
P. O. Box 52034
Phoenix, Arizona 85072-2034
(602) 340-4204
FAX: (602) 250-4989 -- Box 5D

C. D. Churchman
ARIZONA PUBLIC SERVICE
PVNGS
Station 7668
P. O. Box 52034
Phoenix, Arizona 85072-2034
(602) 393-6700

ENGINEERING

Solomon Levy
S. LEVY, INC.
3425 South Bascom Avenue
Campbell, California 95008
(408) 377-4870

Z. J. Elawar
ARIZONA PUBLIC SERVICE
PVNGS
Station 1536
P. O. Box 52034
Phoenix, Arizona 85072-2034
(602) 340-4188
FAX: (602) 250-4989 -- Box 5D

A. C. Rogers
ARIZONA PUBLIC SERVICE
PVNGS
Station 1515
P. O. Box 52034
Phoenix, Arizona 85072-2034
(602) 340-4041
FAX: (602) 250-4989 -- Box 5D

RADIOLOGICAL PROTECTION

T. A. Peterson
427 Noank Road
Mystic, Connecticut 06355
(203) 536-3742
FAX: (203) 536-0782

A. G. Ogurek
ARIZONA PUBLIC SERVICE
PVNGS
Station 1536
P. O. Box 52034
Phoenix, Arizona 85072-2034
(602) 340-4124
FAX: (602) 250-4989 -- Box 5D

ISSUED JULY, 1992

Figure 7.5.   Palo Verde OSRC engineering subcommittee, July 1992.
(Source: Palo Verde)

tions in shutdown cooling lines. In a few cases, the OSRC contributions remained valuable by exerting management pressure to resolve such problems as fuel failures caused by corrosion deposits due to subcooled boiling and axial offset power anomaly.

I enjoyed my long participation on the Palo Verde OSRC because of the mutually satisfactory association developed with a large number of APS employees and managers and because I felt at home whenever I visited the site.

NUCLEAR OVERSIGHT COMMITTEE
AT ONTARIO HYDRO NUCLEAR

In late 1996 and early 1997, the performance of the Ontario Hydro Nuclear (OHN) plants had deteriorated to the point that their board of directors and, in particular, their chairman decided to hire Carl Andognini and a group of talented U.S. personnel to investigate the reasons for the plants' decline and to develop a corrective action plan.

Warren Peabody was in charge of the engineering review. I had worked with Warren before at several other plants and was aware of his great abilities and integrity. Warren chose to carry out safety system functional investigations (SSFI) of various systems at OHN plants to determine the sources of their problems and how to correct them. SSFIs were being performed by the NRC and most U.S. plant owners to determine whether the plant systems still satisfied their licensing basis. The use of SSFIs is a very powerful methodology that provides an integrated perspective of a plant safety system and its deviations from requirements.

Warren wanted me to participate in the SSFIs but other commitments did not allow me to stay away from my office for the two or three weeks needed to complete an SSFI. Instead, I started to look at previous assessments by the OHN Safety Assurance group and to my surprise I found that *many of the safety issues were identified in early internal reports, sometimes several times, with no corrective actions being taken.* Apparently, the safety assurance personnel did not complain high enough or loud enough about the lack of action. Similarly, the Canadian regulator who had access to the same reports did not force corrective action to be taken, as would have happened in the case of the U.S. NRC. As far as I know, *the Canadian regulatory body referred to as the Atomic Energy Control Board (AECB) did not have the authority to shut down a plant and keep it down until they were satisfied by changes made to the plant.* The principal forcing tool in Canada was to reissue the operating license every two years and to use that renewal to get concessions (an extension to five years was granted recently). It appears that *Canada relied on the plant owner/operator to maintain plant safety with much less interference by the regulator.* It is interesting to note that a similar philosophy prevailed with respect to radiation protection and the disposition of spent fuel. I was given an excellent write-up about radiation hazards and about the radiation levels requiring additional protection. However, it was left primarily up to me to decide how to navigate my movement through the plant until the U.S. team recommended more stringent conditions. In the case of spent fuel, the ownership and disposition of Canadian spent fuel remains with the plant owner.

> Canada relied on the plant owner/operator to maintain plant safety with much less interference by the regulator.

The CANDU (CANadian Deuterium natural Uranium) reactors cool their fuel bundles with heavy water (deuterium) flowing in horizontal parallel pressure tubes immersed in heavy water in a calendria vessel instead of the U.S. practice of cooling its vertical fuel with plain water inside a pressure vessel. The Canadians use two fully independent control systems to shut down their reactors and they rely much more on computer than human control to maneuver the plant. The licensing bases use probabilistic arguments to limit the compounding of events and it takes considerably longer to train and license the operators. On the other hand, safety risks of Canadian plants are similar to those of U.S. nuclear plants. As pointed out by the results of the SSFIs, weaknesses were found in many areas such as design configuration control, insufficient protection against fire and postaccident environmental conditions, and limited corrosion inspections to avoid failures, for example, in steam generator tubes. In my opinion, the review of OHN plants could have benefited from increased participation by Canadians to reflect the Canadian safety perspective.

While the safety reviews were being completed, I was asked to join the OHN NOC. The NOC was to have an advisory and fact-finding role for both Ontario Hydro's chief executive officer and for the chief nuclear officer, Carl Andognini. I had worked for Carl previously when

Figure 7.6. OHN Nuclear Oversight Committee. Seated, from left: Dick DeYoung, the author, Carl Andognini, Ken Harris, and Bob Matlock. Standing, from left: Hugh Jamieson, chair of ONH, Malcom Phillips, and Elgin Horton. (Source: Ontario Hydro Nuclear)

he was responsible for the restart of the Rancho Seco nuclear plant of the Sacramento Municipal District. The NOC was to provide a "broad, systematic and independent overview of nuclear safety in Ontario Hydro nuclear facilities."

The members of the NOC are shown in Figure 7.6. They included Bob Matlock who was the chairman of the NOC; next to Bob is Ken Harris, a long-time and very good U.S. nuclear plant manager; next to Ken is Carl Andognini; and I am sitting next to Carl with Dick DeYoung next to me. Dick was a long-time and well-respected licensing director at the U.S. NRC. Standing are Elgin Horton, previously involved with the CANDU OHN design and operation; Malcom Philips, a lawyer from the U.S. firm of Winston & Strawn; the chairman of Ontario Hydro; and Hugh Jamieson who acted as secretary to the NOC. Not shown in the picture is Jack Martin, an ex–regional director of the NRC who joined the NOC a few months later. The NOC held periodic meetings at each plant site and at the headquarters of OHN located in Toronto. The NOC members reported their findings orally to management and the chairman submitted a written report after each meeting.

Ontario Hydro Nuclear was operating a total of 20 nuclear power plants. Eight were located at the Pickering site and produced 515 MWe each. The four oldest plants reached commercial operation in 1971–1973 and the other four plants came online in 1983–1986. Eight other units were located at the Bruce site and one unit of the first four plants was taken offline in 1995 due to contamination. The remaining three units reached commercial operation in 1977–1979 and produced 750 MWe each. The other four Bruce units, each producing 785 MWe came online in 1984–1987. The latest four plants, each producing 881 MWe, are located at the Darlington site and. they became operational in 1990–1993.

As expected, the number of problem areas increased with the age of the plants and the total number of necessary corrective actions was so large that *the only possible solution was to shut down some plants and move their workforce to other plants.* This was not an easy plan to implement due to loss of income from shutdown units, difficulties and costs of relocating personnel from plant to plant, and carrying out modifications while plants remained online. The NOC kept stressing the need for detailed costs and schedules to avoid surprises but accuracy had to be sacrificed due to lengthy and difficult negotiations with the regulatory body and the workers' union. Carl Andognini and the head of the workers' union (who was a member of the board) did not get along very well.

The principal cause of the declining plant performance was attributed to inadequate management and the consequence of that finding was the departure of the chairman of the company. This was unfortunate because he was the person who initiated the assessment and because he was on the board of WANO (World Association of Nuclear Operators) and was the only member of his board with any understanding of nuclear power. Several engineers indicated that the performance decline started when the decision was made to stop construction of more CANDU plants. That led to the loss of knowledgeable engineers/managers and to the reassignment of remaining personnel to the various sites. *The sites became profit centers that emphasized cost reductions.*

Carl Andognini and his team did a remarkable job of recommending changes to plant organization and managers, issuing meaningful management reports, improving the plant safety/capacity factor, and regaining some of the confidence of the regulators. There was some tension between Canadians and Americans, especially due to the large number of American advisers. Also, there were differences in personality. The Americans were loud and told it like it was, whereas the Canadians were more discreet and more willing to accept circumstances. I found the Canadian engineers to be as capable as the U.S. engineers and I was especially impressed by AECL research work. I was surprised by the large number of regulatory issues that didn't have a schedule for resolution and by the late need to recalculate the safety of the Darlington plants during a pump trip and of the Bruce plants during a loss-of-coolant accident.

Due to a loss of electrical generation, the decision was made to restart the early Pickering Unit 4 while the pressure on cost reductions kept rising. During my last visit at the Pickering site, I reviewed the status, schedule, and costs for the restart plan of the shutdown units and concluded that they were inadequate and did not provide for enough changes to satisfy the regulators. OHN appeared to have gone back to their old habits. At the exit meeting, I mentioned my concerns to management but there was little interest in my cautious admonition. At about the same time, the new composition of the board of directors was determined and I noticed that all of the board members had no hands-on experience with nuclear power plants. My previous experience with such boards had convinced me that they would not support a full recovery program and I decided to resign from the NOC.

It is interesting to note that the subsequent mismanagement of the Pickering Unit 4 restart project has received significant attention in Canada because it was two years behind schedule and its cost was triple the original estimate. On July 7, 2004, the decision was made to restart Pickering Unit 1 and the precautions taken are worth mention:

- *All design engineering is complete* compared to 3 percent on unit 4.
- The assessment of the major *construction phase is 86 percent complete* compared to 8 percent for Unit 4 project.
- The *budget including contingency* is Can $900 million compared to one-third that amount for Unit 4.
- A *fully integrated, logically linked, and resource-leveled schedule* with 20,000 tasks is in place compared to a partially completed and unintegrated schedule for Unit 4, which was modified eight times thereafter.

I was pleased to see that the new chairman of the Ontario Power Group (OPG) in 2004 was Jake Epp who was responsible for the review of the Unit 4 problems. I was also elated to see that Gary Kugler, a retired senior vice president of AECL has joined the board because of his involvement in major CANDU nuclear projects. Even though I cannot take credit for any of the most recent changes at OHN, I wish they had happened several years earlier. During my tenure as an NOC member at OHN, I enjoyed working with the other NOC members and all the Canadians associated with CANDU reactors. *I shall always admire their ability to develop, design, construct, and operate a different power reactor design from the U.S. light water reactors.*

> I shall always admire their ability to develop, design, construct, and operate a different power reactor design from the U.S. light water reactors.

GENERAL OFFICE REVIEW BOARD AT OYSTER CREEK, NEW JERSEY

I became a member of the Oyster Creek General Office Review Board (GORB) a few years after leaving GE. The GORB's scope was similar to that of the Palo Verde OSRC. It was chaired by Ivan Finfrock who reported to the board of General Public Utility Nuclear (GPUN). Ivan did an excellent job of moderating the opinions and discussions of the membership, and particularly of the outside members. In December 1982, the outside members were Dr. T. L. Gerber, an excellent materials and structural engineer; D. T. Leighton, a strong instrumentation and control engineer from the nuclear navy; W. W. Lowe, from Pickard, Lowe, & Garrick, a well-known consulting firm; L. H. Roddis, a top lieutenant of Admiral Rickover and formerly the president of Consolidated Edison; Dr. T. M. Snyder from GE, an early pioneer of nuclear power; and myself. Internal members included the plant manager and members of the Engineering, Quality Assurance, and Operations organizations. Presentations were made about key safety issues selected by the chairman and the discussions were allowed to proceed to closure or requests for additional information. The meetings lasted two days and the discussions were usually still going strong when the time came to adjourn.

Because Oyster Creek was the first large BWR to go online, I found the GORB meetings to be of great interest. One problem first observed at Oyster Creek was the *thinning of the pressure suppression containment wall due to corrosion* by sand coming into contact with it. I felt strongly that the degree of thinning and its cause needed investigation and I was asked to make a presentation to the board to support it. Another first was my participation in the team reviewing the Oyster Creek probabilistic risk assessment (PRA) carried out by John Garrick and his team, who appreciated my system knowledge of the plant. After several years on the GORB, I felt that I was beginning to repeat myself and I decided to resign after January 1, 1988.

Even after my resignation was accepted, I was asked to come back and make a presentation on risk management through technical excellence. I have reread it and found it to be applicable more than a decade later.

OTHER REVIEWS OF NUCLEAR POWER PLANTS
Several reviews of nuclear power plants were of shorter duration than those just covered, and a few typical cases are covered next.

FERMI-2 MANAGEMENT COMMITTEE
During the startup of Fermi-2 in Newport, Michigan, there was an inadvertent criticality event as a result of confusing instructions for moving control rod blades. Instead of accepting that fact, the Detroit Edison vice president in charge of the site decided to argue that there was no criti-

cality and I was asked to join an independent management review team chaired by Jack Calhoon who had joined General Physics Corporation after running the Tennessee Valley Authority nuclear program. The scope of the committee was much broader than the criticality event and its final report was very critical of the planning, communications, responsibility assignment, and work output resulting from excessive micromanagement at the top of the site. A new site vice president was appointed and I moved on to become an adviser to the PECO board of directors.

RANCHO SECO ENGINEERING AND OPERATIONAL REVIEW

The engineering restart needs were not being satisfied at the Rancho Seco nuclear plant owned by Sacramento Municipal Utility District (SMUD) and I was asked by Carl Andognini, who was in charge of the recovery program, to head a group to review the situation. *The lack of a list of information required for startup and of an issuance schedule was a large contributor to the problem.* It was solved by appointing a Duke Power assistant manager of engineering dedicated to the development of such a schedule and satisfying it. For example, the contractors who performed most of the work were not allowed to go home for the weekend by the assistant manager until they met their generation of schedule obligations. The team also provided assistance to the manager of engineering by reviewing difficult issues and offering suggestions.

After the team submitted its final report to Andognini, it was asked to carry out a plant restart readiness review. That request was satisfied by having the various Rancho Seco functional managers discuss their readiness status and outstanding issues and plans for their resolution. The team members focused on completeness of issues and assurance of solving outstanding problems.

The NRC eventually agreed to the restart of Rancho Seco but the SMUD board members, who were elected by the public irrespective of their experience and knowledge about nuclear

The goals were not satisfied and the public voted to shut down Rancho Seco when it could have produced a lot of electrical power safely where it was in short supply.

power, established performance goals that would allow a public vote on continued operation if they were not met. *The goals were not satisfied and the public voted to shut down Rancho Seco when it could have produced a lot of electrical power safely where it was in short supply.*

REVIEW OF KOREAN NUCLEAR POWER PLANTS

In the early 1980s, the World Bank asked me to carry out an assessment of South Korea's nuclear program. At first, I was surprised by the World Bank's involvement in nuclear safety but it became understandable right away. The bank had provided considerable funds for South Korean development and the concern was Korea's large dependence on nuclear power and the shutdown of all nuclear generation in the event of a serious accident at one plant.

My flight to Korea had very few passengers because university students were demonstrating against the government at that time and the most violent colleges had been shut down. There was also a night curfew and I was impressed by the presence of a tank and a fully armed soldier standing at its top when I arrived at the Ministry of Power on my first day in that country. An engineer from the power company, KEPCO, was my guide (as well as a good historian) during my entire visit and I was given access to all of their nuclear sites.

I went to the Kori site where a PWR was fully operational and to the Wolsong site where the first Canadian heavy water reactor construction was being completed. I visited the Research Institute, the fuel development facility, the Planning Institute, and the power company. It was clear that all those involved understood the importance of safety. My principal comment was that their *regulatory body was underpaid, understaffed, and not strong or independent enough.* This was important because the regulators were not able to hold their own against the power company, and it would become essential when South Korea stopped relying on the licensing process of the nuclear power plant supplier countries. The report identified several other issues such as slowing down the development of their own design, translating the operating technical specifications into the Korean language to help their understanding by plant operating personnel, and obtaining training simulators to match their plant designs.

My agreement with the World Bank was to refer all questions about the report to the bank and to leave its distribution up to them. I understand that the expectation was for a highly positive report. There was even a leak to the local papers that I was very critical of the Korean nuclear program (which was not the case) and of Bechtel Quality Assurance (I let Bechtel read that portion of the report and they agreed with it). Anyway, the World Bank must have liked the report because they asked me to go back after the TMI accident to review the actions taken by the Korean power plants. This time, I was more critical in such areas as emergency evacuation plans and severe accident management procedures. I also decided *not to perform future safety reviews where I did not see a written corrective action response to my assessment.*

Over the years, I have participated in many more reviews. They are too numerous to even create a list and they range from advice to boards of directors, to topical assessments, to specific technical issues. I have not personally sought that type of work but I have responded when asked unless there was a time conflict. In spite of my increasing age, I still get requests. For example, in 2003 I participated in an assessment of potential vulnerabilities for licensing renewal of the Point Beach Nuclear Plant in Two Rivers, Wisconsin, spearheaded by Jack Martin, and in 2004, I was a member of the phenomena identification and ranking technique (PIRT) applied to the ACR-700 (Advance Canadian Reactor) sponsored by Brookhaven National Laboratory (BNL). On that review, I was a member of the Severe Accident Panel with Mike Corradini, Bob Henry, Dana Powers, and Karen Vierow. Clearly, I enjoyed that type of work and I always felt that I was making a contribution as attested to by the number of requests for my services.

ADVISORY ROLES

Over the years, I have been asked to be an adviser in many instances. Four such typical cases are covered next, including the TMI-2 accident, participation in the INPO Advisory Council, evaluation of the N Reactor, and Generation IV nuclear energy systems.

ADVISORY ROLE AT TMI-2 ACCIDENT

The Three Mile Island 2 nuclear power plant owned by Metropolitan Edison (Met Ed) had a serious accident on March 28, 1979, and I received a phone call from EPRI to come to the site two days later and to help. I left right away, even though I would miss my wife's birthday. Upon my arrival at New York, I rented a car and headed for TMI-2. Close to the plant, I stopped to refill my gasoline tank and to get directions. The attendant pointed out that I was going in the wrong direction and that practically all cars were traveling the opposite way due to an evacuation initiated by the assistant governor of Pennsylvania, which later turned out to be based on incorrect statements about radiation releases from the plant.

> My first and dominant impression was one of confusion because no conclusion had been reached about the cause and consequence of the accident.

At the plant, *my first and dominant impression was one of confusion because no conclusion had been reached about the cause and consequence of the accident.* Plant management personnel were trying to minimize the damage while the press wished for sensational conditions. Several industry icons, such as Bill Lee from Duke Power and Byron Lee from Commonwealth Edison, had reached the site sooner and were discussing how to proceed. An Industry Advisory Group (IAG) was formed and I was assigned to it. Management of the group was under Milt Levenson, who headed the EPRI Nuclear Power Division and who was appointed chairman. Also, a Nuclear Safety Analysis Center (NSAC) was formed at EPRI and Dr. Ed Zebroski was put in charge of analyses and studies to understand and avoid similar accidents. Initially, Ed was the acting chairman of the IAG when Milt was absent. I was the backup chairman when Milt and Ed were absent. With time, I became the acting chairman as Ed spent more time managing NSAC.

Soon after my arrival, I made approximate calculations of the core flow using available temperatures and determined that the *core flow had decreased sharply and that the only possible cause was severe obstruction and damage of the core.* Because some of the temperatures were fluctuating with time, another conclusion drawn was that *pieces of fuel were moving and changing the core configuration.* The debate continued about the topic of fuel melting and while I favored the occurrence of melting, I did not see any merit to further debate about that point because it would be settled only after actual observations of the fuel.

The IAG had several functions. The most important one was to take part in the early morning opening and afternoon closing management meetings. When topics required voting, the IAG had a vote along with votes provided to the NRC, plant owner, and the designer, Babcock & Wilcox (B&W). Practically all decisions were unanimous. I remember only one vote where there was a disagreement and where, as acting IAG chairman, I voted with the NRC. Many important visitors were hosted by the IAG and they were provided a status report and answers to their questions. A few specific technical investigations were assigned to the IAG at the management meetings and the members of IAG generated documented replies.

Almost every day, the chairman of IAG held a meeting with members of the group, where he summarized the management meeting discussions and covered topics assigned to IAG. Members of the IAG consisted of volunteers from industry, university, or government and they were allowed to select study topics of their choice as long as they kept the chairman informed and documented their work. For example, the chairman of ACRS, Joe Palladino, decided to look at the reliability of the off-site power supply and concluded that the highest risk of losing power was from a landing helicopter cutting the power lines. Joe felt strongly enough to contact President Carter and to recommend that the number of helicopter flights to the TMI site be kept to a minimum.

The initial focus at the site was to avoid recriticality of the core and to keep it cool.

The initial focus at the site was to avoid recriticality of the core and to keep it cool. The issue of criticality was resolved by taking periodic samples of primary system cooling water and measuring the boron concentration. This was not an easy task because it involved exposure to a high radiation field and having to ship the samples to an outside laboratory to determine the boron level. I was impressed that plant volunteers were always available to obtain coolant samples and to assure a large margin to criticality. With respect to core cooling, the concern was loss of pumping power and the lack of assurance that natural circulation would keep the core at acceptable temperatures. Because of that uncertainty, *the available plant decay heat removal system could be used to cool the core, but doing so would spread the reactor core contamination beyond the containment.* Also, investigations showed that there was little actual long-term running experience for such systems and it was decided to obtain a backup decay heat removal system from a canceled or delayed nuclear power plant and to install it right next to the containment to increase its accessibility to maintenance. Once a system was located, it was redesigned and flown in a military plane with help from the White House. Vic Stello, who was in charge of NRC decisions at the site, reduced the quality assurance requirements to expedite the design and delivery of the backup system. Decisions were being made in about one-tenth the time needed for normal circumstances. In my opinion, *Vic Stello did not receive the praise he deserved for his numerous on-the-spot decisions during the TMI-2 recovery program.*

The IAG had been firm about not spreading contamination and I was surprised when an angry Vic Stello knocked on the door of my hotel room and wanted to know how the IAG could agree to install a penetration at the top of the containment. When Vic was told that the IAG was never informed about any such plan, he left the room insisting that the IAG be given a line function of reviewing and approving all changes. After further discussion, it was decided that the IAG should remain an advisory body but that it needed to be kept informed about safety issues if it was to fulfill its function.

An important consideration at that time was *whether to use natural circulation to eliminate the reliance on pumping power.* The IAG members participated in all the presentations and reviews of the natural circulation predictions prepared by B&W and the associated assumptions. The decision was made to trip the pumps while they were running satisfactorily in order to restart them if core temperatures continued to rise after the trip. Due to my experience with natural circulation tests at BWR power plants, I was asked to be present during the pump trip at TMI-2, which was scheduled to occur after available core temperature thermocouples were moved and could be read in the control room. My flight from California was slightly delayed and the plant owners sent their helicopter to meet my plane and take me to the site, in spite of Joe Palladino's advice. During the briefing in the control room, there was a short false radiation alarm and we had to put on our respiratory masks. After the all-clear signal, I positioned myself at the core temperature panel and stayed there during the pump trip and until temperatures appear to "stabilize." Some temperatures went up and others went down, while the peak reading remained relatively constant. After a check the following morning that TMI-2 temperatures were stable in a natural circulation mode, it was time to move on to the next phase, that is, to decontaminate the containment and to remove the damaged core. I could be of very little help in that next phase of the recovery.

My involvement with TMI-2, however, did not stop at that point. A member of the Kemeny Commission staff called S. Levy Incorporated and asked for assistance in evaluating the simulation of nuclear power plants. A visit to the B&W simulator was arranged because it was the facility where the TMI-2 operators were trained. To my great surprise, *it was found that the B&W simulator employed a single liquid-phase model and did not provide for steam or hydrogen presence.* In other words, *if steam or hydrogen gas were generated in the core while water was being added, the operators were trained to believe that too much water was coming in and they would turn off the emergency cooling water as they did. Operators were never told that a gas or steam bubble in the core could also lead to a water level rise in the pressurizer.*

The Kemeny Commission staff member was from NASA and he arranged for a visit to the space center in Texas. It was impressive to visit the control center and to hear how it would react during an emergency. The information received from the space flight was extensive and large computer systems were available to assess flight conditions. The contrast with circumstances in the TMI-2 control room was striking. *Most nuclear plant operators did not have the ability to evaluate or analyze their reactor core performance in real time or to specify the consequences of accidents in terms of their frequency of occurrence.* I presented those concerns in an invited lecture at the ASME annual meeting in December 1980, which was published in *Heat Transfer Engineering* (Volume 1, Number 4, April/ June 1980). For example, the accident at TMI-2 was initiated by a loss of feed-water, which has a probability of occurring once per year. The plant was designed so that a relief valve would open and close to reduce the reactor pressure rise and to avoid a plant shutdown. The possibility of a relief valve's opening and failing to close is estimated to be once out of every 20 times, which means that *TMI-2 was designed to have a loss-of-coolant accident the size of a relief valve with a probability of once in 20 years because the valve was not instrumented to detect its failure to close.* Instrumentation was installed after the accident to reduce that probability to about once every 2000 years, which may still be too high depending on the break size involved.

> **Most nuclear plant operators did not have the ability to evaluate or analyze their reactor core performance in real time or to specify the consequences of accidents in terms of their frequency of occurrence.**

An EPRI report, NSAC-1, provides an excellent description of the conditions prevailing during the early phase of the TMI-2 accident. According to that evaluation, *70 important operator actions had to occur before core cooling approached relatively stable conditions. The design process had put little emphasis on analyzing enough smaller breaks involving human/ machine interactions* and instead focused on the highly improbable very large break. The TMI-2 accident changed all that and finally assured that smaller breaks would receive their proper share of evaluations as suggested by the AEC's Emergency Core Cooling Task Force in 1966. *Because human/machine interactions have an important safety role, it is essential that real-time simulations with factual hardware models be available to train operators and their supervisors.*

The accident at TMI-2 has been subjected to numerous reviews which have generated many recommendations to improve the safety of nuclear power plants. The creation of INPO with its emphasis on training, information exchange between plants, and the pursuit of excellence are especially noteworthy. The other consequences of the accident were loss of industry credibility, considerable delays in construction of nuclear power plants and a significant increase in their costs. *In the United States, that impact is still being felt because more than 25 years have passed since the accident at TMI-2 and consideration is just now being given to the idea of building new nuclear power plants.* My participation in that event was minimal but it has left an indelible impression on me and my nuclear power consulting work.

ADVISORY ROLE AT INPO

The nuclear electric industry formed the Institute of Nuclear Operations in 1979, shortly after the TMI-2 accident. *INPO's mission is to promote the highest levels of safety and reliability—to promote excellence—in the operation of nuclear electric generating plants.* In 1993, I became a member of the INPO Advisory Council with the help of my good friend Dennis Wilkinson who was selected to be the first president of INPO. I complained often to Dennis that INPO was not paying enough attention to the engineering design of nuclear power plants and he decided to have me join the advisory council. The council met periodically and spent an entire day discussing topics selected by the members of the council and the president of INPO during my tenure, Zack Pate.

The composition of the council was diverse and included university personnel (N. E. Todreas from the Massachusetts Institute of Technology (MIT) and R. L. Seale from the University of Arizona), lawyers (J. R. Curtiss), financial people (R. Gilham from Chase Manhattan Bank), people from other industries (D. M. Carlton from Radian Corporation, J. K. Lauber from Delta Air Lines, and E. A. Womack from McDermott International), participants in the nuclear industry (W. F. Conway, formerly from Palo Verde, and R. C. Franklin, formerly from Ontario Hydro), consultants (A. C. Daniels and F. J. Remick), and others (E. J. George from the Iowa Utilities Board and W. Sinclair from the National Council on Radiation). That varied membership generated interesting and challenging discussions on such topics as publication of INPO performance assessments, use of risk methodology, managerial development, and cost competitiveness.

Members were asked to submit outlines and charts of their material to be distributed to other members of the Council. On January 12, 1993, I made a presentation titled "Radical Strategies to Reduce Nuclear Power Plant Generation Costs" and I was lucky to predict the consolidation that occurred several years later. It also encouraged, as promised to Dennis Wilkinson, increased involvement of INPO in design engineering, but INPO remained comfortable dealing primarily with the operational side of engineering, or systems engineering.

INPO had four cornerstone technical programs: evaluation programs, training and accreditation programs, events analysis and information exchange programs, and assistance to members. My first assignment after joining the Advisory Council was to observe the performance evaluation being carried out at Portland General Electric's Trojan nuclear plant in Oregon. I was impressed by the degree of review performed by the evaluation team before arriving at the site. They had gone through the Trojan and the NRC progress reports and they had determined the weakness areas on which to focus. All findings were to be supported by specific examples and reviewed with plant personnel.

Daily team meetings were held to go over status of review and I sat in on all such get-togethers while at the plant. I accompanied the water chemistry reviewer because the plant steam generator tubes were exhibiting several defects requiring tube plugging and replacement of the steam generators in the near future. It was clear that the plant water chemistry had been inadequate and that the Trojan program needed upgrading. The INPO assessment was conducted very professionally. I felt that the experience and leadership of the team leader were important to the success of the evaluation program, and I so reported to the council. It was unfortunate that it was not done much earlier to correct its water chemistry because the plant was eventually shut down due to a debate about the costs of replacing its steam generators.

I also had a chance to comment about the events analysis and information exchange cornerstone program. My initial comments reflected the views of plants where I was a member of the Safety Review Committee. The INPO information system was also exercised for primary system pumps and I was surprised by the small amount of information available, considering the fact that the Palo Verde pumps had had many difficulties during plant startup. Several months later, I was asked to participate in an independent review of the INPO information data-base. The review team included plant managers and INPO personnel, and the team visited three nuclear power plants. The results of the review tended to be negative and emphasized the need for a much more user-friendly system, which INPO agreed to imple-ment. In my last presentation to the council, I was very cautious about the use of risk-based licensing systems because of the concern that the NRC would use both risk and nonrisk systems and apply the more conservative of the two approaches. I was wrong in that forecast and I am glad to admit it today because *risk-informed methodology has been of great benefit to nuclear plants.*

> **Risk-informed methodology has been of great benefit to nuclear plants.**

Over the years, I have read many INPO performance reports and I believe that the great improvements in the INPO performance indicators can be traced to the INPO assessments. *Obtaining a top INPO rating became the objective of every nuclear power plant* and INPO made sure that progress was being made by obtaining an improvement plan and verifying that it was being carried out from one assessment to the next. The inclusion of peer reviewers and the application of good practices helped the pursuit of excellence. The open exchange of information between plants was remarkable because it put safety ahead of economic competition

ADVISORY ROLE AT THE N REACTOR

My involvement with the N production reactor at Hanford, Washington, started shortly after the April 1986 accident at the Chernobyl nuclear station in the Soviet Union. A small team headed by Lou Roddis was formed to determine whether the N Reactor should be restarted. I was a member of the team with Dana Powers from Sandia National Laboratory. With respect to the Chernobyl event, the safety issue at the N Reactor was the presence of a confinement instead of a containment system. *The confinement was designed to vent before the pressure exceeded 5 psig and to use a filter after the vent, but it had little capability to detect and miti-gate hydrogen releases and their combustion.* Based on that shortcoming, Roddis was adamant about not restarting the N Reactor. I agreed with that position but my vote was more influenced by aging problems at that facility.

The N Reactor was a graphite-moderated unit and it used pressurized water to cool the metallic uranium fuel clad with Zircaloy held in horizontal tubes to produce weapons-grade plutonium and to generate steam for electricity. Due to radiation, *the graphite was expanding nonuniformly and was applying stresses on the horizontal fuel process tubes and the graphite cooling tubes.* Four process tubes had failed previously and additional indications were found on numerous tubes by inspection. An end-of-life estimate to occur between 1991 and 1996 had been generated due to graphite expansion but the damage to process tubes was anticipated to shut down the N Reactor much earlier than 1991. *Lou Roddis issued a strong letter to the secretary of energy, dated October 3, 1986, recommending permanent shutdown of the reactor.*

ADVISORY ROLE ON GENERATION IV NUCLEAR ENERGY SYSTEMS

In early 2000, an International Workshop on Generation IV Nuclear Energy Systems was convened by the United States. Representatives from nine countries attended and agreed to form a Generation IV International Forum (GIF) dedicated to the development by 2030 of the next generation of nuclear reactor and fuel cycle technologies. The Nuclear Energy Research Advisory Committee (NERAC) to DOE chartered a subcommittee referred to as the *Gen IV Roadmap NERAC Subcommittee (GRNS)* to establish goals and provide advice to DOE on the preparation of such a roadmap. My good friend, Neal Todreas, from MIT asked me to cochair the GRNS with him. The organization of the Roadmap project and the composition of GRNS are illustrated in Figure 7.7. GRNS was fortunate to attract Bobby Abrams and William Naughton from the nuclear power industry; Ted Marston, who was in charge of the EPRI Nuclear Division; John Garrick, who performed the first commercial probabilistic risk assessment for nuclear power plants;

ROADMAP
MEMBERS OF THE GENERATION IV ROADMAP PROJECT

Generation IV
Roadmap NERAC Subcommittee (GRNS)

Bobby Abrams[f]
Duke Engineering

Douglas Chapin
MPR Associates

B. John Garrick
Independent Consultant

Daniel Kammen
University of California–Berkeley

Salomon Levy[g]
Levy & Associates

Ted Marston
Electrical Power Research Institute

William Naughton
Exelon

Neil Todreas[g]
Massachusetts Institute of Technology

Roadmap Integration Team (RIT)

Todd Allen
Argonne National Laboratory

Ralph Bennett[g]
Idaho National Engineering and Environmental Laboratory

Gian Luigi Fiorini
Commissariat à l'Energie Atomique

Hussein Khalil[g]
Argonne National Laboratory

John Kotek
Argonne National Laboratory

John M. Ryskamp
Idaho National Engineering and Environmental Laboratory

Rob Versluis
Department of Energy – Nuclear Energy

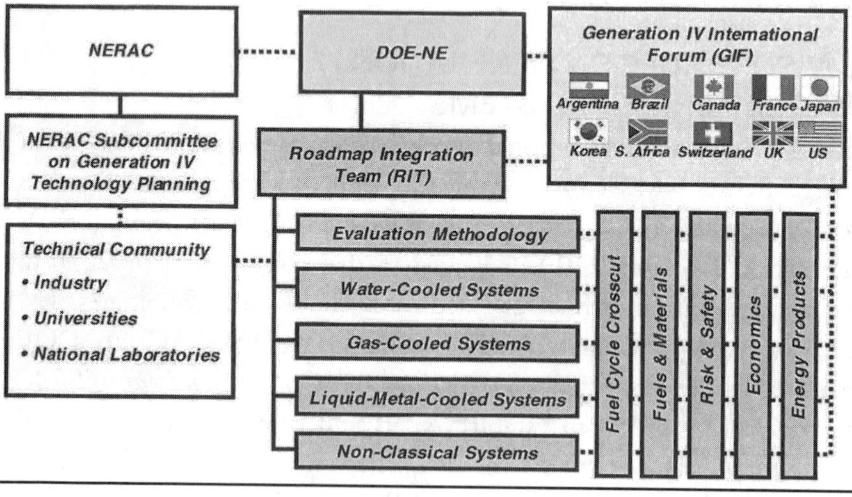

Figure 7.7.   GRNS organizational chart. (Source: Roadmap Report, GIF-002-00, 2002)

Doug Chapin, a well-known consultant from MPR Associates; and Dan Kammen, a professor at UCB and a supporter of renewable energy sources.

The first task of the GRNS was to develop a set of goals for Generation IV. After two drafts and considerable comments from DOE, the GIF members, and independent experts, *eight goals were defined in the areas of sustainability, economics, safety and reliability, proliferation resistance, and physical protection.* In addition, the GRNS provided considerable support to a complementary program addressing near-term deployment in the United States by having two of its members participate in those deliberations and by offering comments about the *Roadmap to Deploy New Nuclear Power Plants in the United States by 2010.* Longer term, the objective was to develop a technology roadmap that would identify the research and development (R&D) needed to advance the most promising Generation IV nuclear energy systems.

A Roadmap Integration Team to direct the work and a group to develop an evaluation methodology to assess proposed concepts and associated fuel cycles were formed initially, and a solicitation was issued worldwide for concepts satisfying some or all the goals. About 100 responses were received and four technical working groups arranged by reactor type were appointed to review the submittals. A Fuel Cycle Crosscut Group was added to evaluate the impact of potential fuel cycles. Later, other crosscut groups were formed to help with consistency and the R&D needs. Half the members of the various groups came from the international GIF members and a total of about 100 experts were involved in the formulation of the roadmap. A GRNS member was assigned to each group to participate in their meetings, and the GRNS held periodic meetings to review overall progress and provide comments to DOE. One of the two cochairs of GRNS also attended the GIF meetings that were held in foreign countries.

The time and the number of trips involved under GRNS were much greater than anticipated. No new promising concept was generated but the groundwork was laid to reach agreement on joint international development programs. A total of six concepts were selected by GIF. Two of the concepts made the list because they had an increased thermodynamic cycle efficiency as a result of using high-temperature gas and water above critical pressure. Three other concepts were selected because they used a fast neutron spectrum to manage the actinides formed in spent fuel; they used sodium, lead, and gas as coolants. The last concept was a very high gas temperature concept that produced hydrogen.

DOE appeared to be more interested in reaching a consensus about the selected concepts rather than in exerting leadership by reflecting its views and those of the U.S. nuclear industry. Some of the GRNS members kept pointing out that some concepts would not be accepted by the U.S. nuclear industry, but that suggestion was rejected. Also, I was especially disappointed to find out that DOE was formulating an advanced fuel cycle study without involving GRNS, even though the Generation IV sustainability goals dealt with "effective fuel utilization" and the need to "minimize and manage nuclear waste and to notably reduce its long-term stewardship burden." The issuance of the two road-maps, the short-term one by October 2001 and the long-term one by December 2002, brought GRNS involvement to an end and all of the members were glad to see it happen because, for conflict of interest reasons, they were serving with no pay. In spite of that pro bono circumstance, I enjoyed my participation on GRNS, even though I was sometimes frustrated by the domestic and international politics that entered the word-smithing process with respect to fuel reprocessing and actinide management.

INVOLVEMENT IN CONTAINMENT LOAD LAWSUIT

Personally, I was involved as a defendant for GE in one lawsuit about the loads produced in BWR pressure suppression containment systems. BWR containment systems were discussed in Chapter 5 and I was involved with them while I was responsible for Design Engineering at GE and for their Boiling Water Reactor Systems Department and the Boiling Water Reactor Operations.

After the BWR containment changes had been approved by the NRC and implemented in the field, some of the utilities tried to recover the costs of the modifications from GE. At that time, I had been gone from

GE for six or seven years and I agreed to provide videotaped testimony for GE with the understanding that I would not participate in any case going to trial. Henry Bose acted as my lawyer and we were both paid our normal service rates by GE. Most of the complaints came from nuclear system sales for which GE did not supply the containment. In the case of turnkey projects still under construction or under the one-year equipment warranty beyond full-power operation, GE made the necessary modifications and reached agreement about their costs with plant owners. For nuclear system sales, the equipment warranty did not apply to the containment because it was not listed under the GE equipment supply scope.

During my many depositions, I kept offering my nonlegal opinion that I did not see why GE would be liable for the containment system cost increases since GE had received no payment for the design modifications to those systems. The argument was then made that GE was the only organization with the necessary knowledge to design the containment. It was true that GE had offered to calculate the containment design pressure under a separate subcontract and did so in many cases. However, Stone & Webster, one of the architect-engineers responsible for some of the BWR projects, had developed their own methodology for predicting comparable containment pressures. Furthermore, the containment changes were not related to its design pressure but to air/steam flow through the drywell vents after a loss-of-coolant accident or by relief valves opening and exhausting their air/steam supply into the suppression pool. To be more precise, it was the unrealistic combination of all such loads with seismic loads by the regulators that contributed most to the changes. *Those combinations did not take into account the fact that the possibility of a double-ended instantaneous large pipe break was extremely remote and that to combine it with a large seismic event and the opening of relief valves was unrealistic.*

> The possibility of a double-ended instantaneous large pipe break was extremely remote.

During my deposition, the opposition lawyers attempted to blame the inadequate treatment of loads on the high competition for nuclear orders and the fast pace of BWR evolution. Those lawyers were smiling and happy with my good recollection of BWR development. They became concerned when I went on to recount the comparable set of PWR developments: increased specific power, addition of soluble poison, use of finger control rods, and water chemistry changes. That list showed that the PWR had undergone just as many improvements as the BWR. That was the end of that set of lawyers who, I believe unintentionally, agreed with my overall assessment of industry development.

The next set of lawyers was provided with good historical background about the NRC's principal concern with respect to keeping the containment pressure below the design value, which required complete condensation of the steam reaching the suppression pool. GE tests had developed accurate instructions about the depth of submergence of the vents to ensure condensation and they were always satisfied. Vibrations were also reported at higher pool temperatures and design precautions were taken to avoid them. Those actions prevented the damage observed in a German power plant when opening of relief valves was allowed to exceed the GE temperature limit. In the case of relief valves, it was noted that they were opened during full-power load rejection start-up tests, which showed the structural impact to be acceptable. I was questioned for many days and I have to admit that some of my responses were not well organized or clear and that I had the bad habit of offering comments beyond the questions being asked. Also, I did not avoid responding to questions by relying on the "do not recall" strategy.

Eventually, one of the utilities, Washington Public Power Supply System (WPPSS), decided to go to trial in Phoenix, Arizona. That is when I received a phone call from Jack Welch, GE president, to tell me that the GE lawyers had been very tough on Dale Bridenbaugh, the GE containment load project engineer and one of the three engineers who had resigned abruptly from GE as discussed in Chapter 5. Apparently, Bridenbaugh cried while he was on the stand, which was expected to influence the jury in his favor.

After a review of GE depositions, lawyers recommended that I be the lead-off witness. My first reaction was to decline, but GE had treated me very well except when I was forced to take on the Boiling Water Reactor

Systems Department, and I decided that it was important to defend the credibility of my GE engineers. I was instructed by the judge not to bring up the corrective actions implemented in Japan, but those conditions were mentioned by the WPPSS lawyers, so the judge then allowed me to summarize them. The questioning tried next to show that I knew about the issues while I was in charge of engineering even though I was the general manager of the Fuel Department when the issue surfaced. I described the *GE procedure available to employees to raise a safety issue and the management process to respond to it.* I stated that no containment safety issue was raised to my level and that I was not aware of receiving a copy of

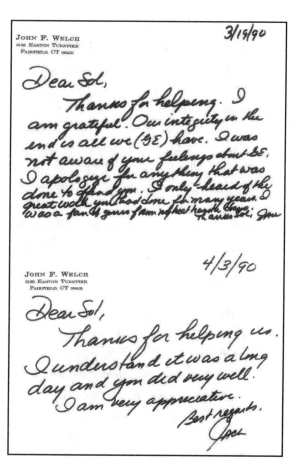

Figure 7.8. Appreciative postcards from Jack Welch, then president of GE. (Courtesy of Jack Welch)

a letter where it was mentioned, nor could the WPPSS lawyers produce such a letter. The last question addressed to me was: "Doctor Levy, as a member of the Academy of Engineering, do you have any regret about the load issue?" My reply was "I wish it had come up earlier so that it could have been resolved sooner."

Figure 7.8 shows the two postcards I received from Jack Welch in which he thanks me for my involvement, and they allow me a chance to comment on his tremendous management skills. The Phoenix trial ended with a hung jury and the case was dismissed. Considering the enormous costs of another trial, WPPSS reached a settlement with GE to provide services at reduced rates. I understand that similar arrangements were made with other customers.

My only other involvement with containment loads was to explain and defend the modifications for Philadelphia Electric's Limerick plant in their efforts to recover those costs from the State Power Authority. My opponent was Steve Hanauer, formerly from the NRC, and the Philadelphia Electric lawyers were shocked when I walked over to his table to shake his hand. After all, I had known Steve for many years and we respected each other during that time. Incidentally, Philadelphia Electric's additional costs were allowed by the presiding judge.

TECHNICAL CONTRIBUTIONS

ANNULAR TWO-PHASE FLOW

Shortly after leaving GE, I went back to modeling two-phase (gas-liquid) annular flow and I was surprised to find out that my absence from that field had not wiped out my ability to write complex equations and solve them. It just took longer because I made more mistakes!

A proposal was made to EPRI in 1988 to develop a critical heat flux prediction model from the analytical annular model. Dr. Bill Sun sponsored that work and allowed me to work on a flexible schedule. A total of four EPRI reports (EPRI NP-1409, 1521, 1563, and 1619) were issued from May to November 1980 and they led to two publications in state-of-the-art technical magazines to confirm my comeback.

ADVANCE CODE REVIEW

I was next contacted to participate in an advance code review being conducted by Dr. L. S. Tong who was in charge of thermal hydraulics for the NRC Research Branch. Tong had held an early position at Westinghouse that was similar to mine at GE at that time and we knew each other very well, even though, at heat transfer technical meetings, we seldom talked about nuclear power for competitive reasons.

NRC had created an Advanced Code Review Committee and I was asked by Dr. Tong to become a member. The committee function was to review the *Los Alamos work to develop the transient reactor analysis code, TRAC, for predicting loss-of-coolant accidents (LOCAs) in PWRs.* The Los Alamos personnel were very good at writing code software and developing the stable methodology required to solve the nonlinear conservation equations involved. The committee members were well known for their relevant research work and for identifying sources of data to compare to the predictions. It is important to note that the data were obtained in separate effects tests often under steady-state conditions and that they were utilized under transient conditions involving other phenomena.

These periodic meetings gave me a chance to hear about the latest experiments and about the approximations needed to codify the complex two-phase flow phenomena. The Los Alamos engineers were not as appreciative of attending the review meetings because *they were getting tired of being told that they could not sacrifice the physics involved to simplify their computer simulations.*

> They could not sacrifice the physics involved to simplify their computer simulations.

PRESSURIZED THERMAL SHOCK

In 1982, I was exposed to the issue of pressurized thermal shock (PTS) due to the addition of cold water to a PWR with highly irradiated pressure vessel walls. I made the mistake of developing an oversimplified model assuming no recirculation flow and complete mixing of the added cold water with the inventoried water at full pressure in the vessel. The model predicted acceptable exponential decreases of temperatures and I was drafted into the PTS workshops. Figure 7.9 shows the large and impressive number of participants from industry, EPRI, and NRC and contractors in October 1982. Also included are Creare engineers who were responsible for the reduced-scale experiments being performed. This issue was eventually resolved by developing two- and three-dimensional models to match the test data.

BEST ESTIMATE SAFETY ANALYSIS

In September 1988, the *NRC approved a revised rule for the acceptance of emergency core cooling systems (ECCSs) using best estimate methodology*

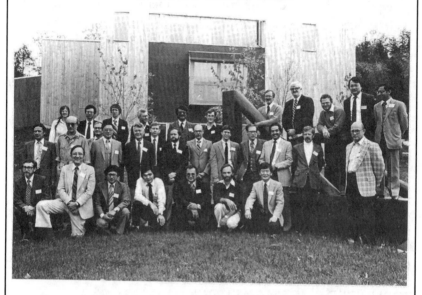

ELECTRIC POWER RESEARCH INSTITUTE
Nuclear Power Division

Workshop on PTS Fluid and Thermal Mixing
Creare R&D Inc., Etna Road, Hanover, New Hampshire
October 7 and 8, 1982

Photo Key

List of Attendees

1. Ackerson, S (W)
2. Block, James A. (Creare)
3. Catton, Ivan (UCLA)
4. Chao, Jason (EPRI)
5. Chen, Brian (ANL)
6. Fanning, Margaret W. (Creare)
7. Habert, Roger (Yankee Atomic)
8. Hashemi, Ab (SAI)
9. Hassan, Yassin (B&W)
10. Hochreiter, Larry (W)
11. Hsu, Chin (Con Edison)
12. Jageler, Ernest (C–E)
13. Kim, Jong (EPRI)
14. Koontz, David (Duke Power)
15. Lauben, Norm (NRC)
16. Levy, Salomon (SLI)
17. Lyczkowski, Bob (ANL)
18. McGriff, Bob (EPRI)
19. Menzel, Gerhart (C–E)
20. Oh, Seung (Jaycor)
21. Phillips, Jerry (CP&L)
22. Preliewicz, Dan (BG&E)
23. Rothe, Paul H. (Creare)
24. Rupprecht, Sandy (W)
25. Sengupta, Subrata, Dr. (FP&L)
26. Sha, Bill (ANL)
27. Singhel, Ashok (Cham)
28. Sun, Bill (EPRI)
30. Valenzuela, Javier A. (Creare)
31. Walters, Frank (B&W)
32. Zuber, Novak (NRC)

Not pictured:
Sursock, Jean-Pierre (EPRI)

Figure 7.9.   PST workshop participants, October 1982. (Courtesy of EPRI, 1982)

and requiring the uncertainty in the calculations to be provided. A technical program group was formed to develop the proper methodology. It was headed by Dr. Novak Zuber of the NRC and included eight other knowledgeable individuals from national laboratories, academia, and industry. I was originally the only member of industry to participate, but I obtained the help of Drs. Gerry Lellouche and Randy May of SLI for the uncertainty analysis toward the end of the project. A systematic and comprehensive methodology called Code Scaling, Applicability, and Uncertainty (CSAU) was formulated over 15 months and subjected to review by a peer group and the ACRS. Credit for its development belongs to Dr. Zuber who insisted on a structured, auditable, and traceable methodology. I strongly supported the need for complete code documentation and freezing the code version or showing that the changes did not influence previous verifications.

When the topic of nodalization came up, the work came to a stop due to studies by Sandia to try to optimize the size of the nodes. I kept pointing out that *the size of the nodes and assumptions used to develop correlations in separate effect tests must be preserved when they are applied to the transient analysis of power plants.* For example, the critical heat flux correlation for BWR fuel assemblies is obtained using the inlet flow and mixed mean steam quality in prototypic electrically heated fuel assemblies and the same approach must be preserved in the reactor analysis. If, on the other hand, the critical heat flux correlation employs local flows and steam qualities calculated with a multidimensional two-phase computer code, that same computer code must be used for the power plant, and the size of the nodes needs to be the same as for the derivation of the correlation. Another example would be to use TRAC to predict the simulated LOCA in the electrically heated Semi-Scale Facility. If the node size was adjusted in TRAC or other changes were made to the code to get a better fit to the Semi-Scale results, those changes must be preserved in the plant analysis. An alternative is to go back and use the plant node to predict the Semi-Scale results and to account for the difference between test and prediction as

> The CSAU methodology should be required reading by all system computer code analysts.

an uncertainty in the plant best estimate analysis. I have dwelled on the nodalization topic to emphasize that *plant nodalization is not arbitrary but controlled by experience and the key tests used to support TRAC. The CSAU methodology is described well in NUREG/CR-5249 and it should be required reading by all system computer code analysts.* I consider that report to be important and valuable because it allowed the use of best estimate predictions and defined their uncertainties.

SEVERE ACCIDENT SCALING METHODOLOGY

After the success of the CSAU, the NRC decided to pursue a *severe accident scaling methodology* (SASM). A technical program group (TPG) consisting of 17 knowledgeable participants was formed with Dr. Novak Zuber as its chairman. The members came from the NRC, four national laboratories, four universities, EPRI, and industry. I was one of the industry members and Dr. Jim Healzer of SLI who substituted for me became another member.

As a result of this study, Dr. Zuber was able to develop a powerful *hierarchically two-tiered scaling* (H2TS) methodology. One tier is based on the top-down or system approach and the other on the bottom-up or process approach. In addition, the phenomena involved were identified, assessed, and their order of importance established by members of the TPG. The approach was applied to a PWR very severe loss-of-power accident that is allowed to proceed at full pressure until a melt takes place in the core and penetrates the reactor vessel at its bottom. The melt is ejected through the cavity tunnel and entrained material reaches the containment to increase its pressure. This severe accident has been called *direct containment heating* (DCH).

SASM was used to define three scale experiments at Sandia National Laboratories. They were able to show that containment failure was avoidable when the amount of melt ejected, its metallic content, and the percentage of entrained material were not overly extreme and all the heat-producing mechanisms were not additive. This TPG was much larger and did not work together as well as the CSAU group. The draft report of NUREG/CR-5809 ended up with a number of dislocated appendices. I still, remember trying to reconcile two vocal members of

Figure 7.10. Technical program group on severe accident scaling methodology. From left: F. Eltawila, NRC; NRC engineer; M. Pilch, Sandia; G. Wilson, INEL; B. Boyack, LANL; B. Sehgal, EPRI; S. Levy, SLI; T. Theofanous, UCSB; A. Dukler, University of Houston; and W. Wulff, BNL. (Source: S. Levy Incorporated)

the group who used to be very friendly before SASM arrived. The TPG held one of its meetings at SLI offices and a picture of several members is reproduced in Figure 7.10. The resolution of the DCH issue came about due to Dr. Zuber's insistence on the use of scaling methodology and the excellent experimental work under Dr. Pilch at Sandia, which allowed the formulation of a model to show that the probability of a dry containment failure was very remote.

MELT ATTACK AND COOLABILITY EXPERIMENTS

I participated in another important severe accident program. It was called the *melt attack and coolability experiments* (MACE) program. It consisted of performing tests with prototypical molten corium materials interacting at the bottom with the basemat of the containment and with water being added at the top. It was presumed that the water would cool the corium and terminate its interaction with the concrete. I was invited by Dr. Raj Sehgal, who was in charge of the program at EPRI, to participate in the design review of an early MACE test and I continued to act as a consultant to the experiments until their end in 2002. At that time, I was asked to draft a summary report which was coauthored by the Argonne National Laboratory (ANL) principal investigator, Mitch Farmer.

The MACE tests were very difficult experiments carried out with prototypical corium materials at very high temperatures. The credit for the test results belongs to ANL personnel and to Bill Spencer and Mitch Farmer who managed the program. A total of five tests were performed successfully, three with limestone/common sand concrete, one with siliceous concrete, and a separate effect test with an inert basemat and an externally supplied gas source.

All of the experiments exhibited the same cooling mechanisms. When water was added atop the molten corium, a large amount of energy, referred to as *bulk cooling,* was extracted from the corium due to the increased contact surface area between melt and water; solidified corium particles were produced and they formed a *stable crust* porous enough to allow venting of the concrete decomposition gases; *crust separation* from the melt took place shortly after its formation because the melt pulled away due to concrete densification on melting and mechanical bonding of the crust to the sidewalls to support it. If the heat supplied to the melt was high enough, melt dispersal above the crust occurred by ejection of particles by sparging gases or by lava flows or melt extrusions through the crust; as the melt and crust separation and the crust thickness increased with time, *water ingression into crust via fissures or porosity* became the only mechanism to achieve coolability unless there was a mechanical crust breach to flood the melt below. Two such crust failures occurred in the MACE tests: (1) In the case of a siliceous concrete basemat, a hole 3 × 5 cm formed in the top crust shortly after water was added and led to water coming into contact with the bottom of the top crust, and (2) when the test section was enlarged from 50 × 50 cm to

120×120 cm, about one-third of the suspended crust failed and relocated downward.

In the MACE tests heat was applied only to the melt and it needed to be reduced as the amount of melt material was reduced by several mechanisms: sidewall and top melt surface attachment before water addition, formation of a self- supporting crust and its growth with time, debris beds formed above the crust, and lava flows or melt extrusion through the crust. That information was not available to the operators during the test and often was obtained only after posttest observations and analyses. The result was to overpower the melt and to increase the loss of material by more melt ejections and additional growth of the crust, which further raised the specific power of the melt and lowered the water crust ingression.

There was only one MACE test, MACE M1b, where the specific power of the melt was kept relatively constant as it would be in a nuclear power plant. In MACE M1b, coolability was achieved with the help of strong bulk cooling due to metallics in the melt and the formation of a crust with increased porosity. The other possibility to terminate the melt concrete interaction was to show that *a self-supporting crust would not form in the power plant because its basemat would have a surface area 20 to 60 times larger than in the largest 120- × 120-cm MACE test.* Analyses and measurements of the MACE crust strengths are given in the summary report to support that contention, but I still regret that a test at 150×150 cm could not be carried out (for cost reasons) as recommended by a special team I headed.

Finally, arguments were made that should be mentioned about the reality of the test configuration used in the MACE program. The concept of having a uniform melt covering the basemat and beginning to attack the concrete is much less likely than having the melt ejected from the vessel at high pressure and being mostly entrained into the containment or having the melt fall into a water pool, which would enhance bulk cooling and produce much more porous particles to enhance water ingression.

> The MACE program convinced me that prototypical experiments of severe accidents would be very costly and very difficult to carry out.

It is obvious that I found *the MACE program very challenging technically. It convinced me that prototypical experiments of severe accidents would be very costly and very difficult to carry out.* I remain frustrated that a definitive demonstration of coolability was not achieved. I am convinced that *adding water to corium attacking the containment concrete basemat is the correct strategy for no other reason than that it will provide a significant filter to the release of fission products contained in the corium.*

YUCCA MOUNTAIN REVIEW

As the work on the Yucca Mountain repository for nuclear waste gained momentum, I was contacted by Ray Durante, a former Westinghouse vice president, to join a committee to review the design of the waste package and surface facilities to be used for disposal of power reactor spent fuel. I agreed to attend periodic meetings where progress on the design work would be presented and the members of the committee would prepare comments on the information received. In addition to Ray and myself, the review group's other members included Dr. Peter Andresen, from GE Corporate Research Laboratory; Dr. David Shoesmith, from AECL and the University of Western Ontario in Canada; Jack Lemley, CEO of American Ecology Corporation; and Larry Snyder from Snyder Engineering. Andresen and Shoesmith are renowned for their work on materials corrosion and chemistry, while Lemley and Snyder are knowledgeable about drilling tunnels and drifts where the waste packages will be emplaced.

I found this assignment to be of great interest because it involved a *different type of water flow through soil below the top surface of the earth but above the water table, which is referred to as the vadose zone.* My bookcase now contains several books about the processes, science, and technology solutions in the vadose zone but my comments were limited to such issues as disliking the use of ventilation in the emplacement drifts because of the difficulties of remotely maintaining the equipment for hundreds of years. I also favored running the repository hot, in disagreement with the position of the Nuclear Waste Technical Review Board, because it would stop water from reaching the waste packages. I wrote a strong memorandum about controlling the computer system codes being used and the importance of documenting changes and their validation. I suggested several times that *DOE should provide plant owners with DOE waste packages so that they could be loaded at the plants to avoid the unloading of shipping casks and the retransfer of spent fuel into waste packages at Yucca.* I stated that *releasing all the fission products in a specified number of waste packages was extreme even for a volcanic eruption* because power plant studies and tests had shown that only a small fraction would escape and the release source term used in the licensing of nuclear power plants had declined over the years. I still believe that this may be the best way to resolve the peak dose issue occurring after 10,000 years. I indicated that the interference between temperature fields from adjoining emplacement drifts should be kept to a minimum to simplify the analysis and that recommendation was accepted.

My involvement with the Yucca Mountain project stopped when TRW lost its contract to manage it. My frustration level was high at that time *because I had reached the conclusion that DOE was having difficulties managing a very large project such as Yucca Mountain. It lacked stability, a definitive organization, a strong manager and relied on too many subcontractors and advisers.* So, I did not mind not being asked back by Bechtel/SAIC, the two new companies in charge, after attending two review meetings.

> **DOE was having difficulties managing a very large project such as Yucca Mountain.**

Note: Several of the views expressed in the preceding Technical Contributions section were summarized in a review paper titled "The Important Role of Thermal Hydraulics in 50 Years of Nuclear Power Application" presented in 1993 in Grenoble, France, and published in *Nuclear Engineering and Design* (Volume 149, pp. 1–10, 1994).

THERMAL-HYDRAULIC BOOK PROJECT

Before closing the coverage of my consulting years, I need to mention the work that gave me the greatest pleasure during that time: writing a book titled *Two-Phase Flow in Complex Systems* after I resigned as president of S. Levy Incorporated (SLI). During my move from the SLI building to a separate office, I found my typed notes of two-phase flow lectures

Figure 7.11.   S. Levy's *Two-Phase Flow in Complex Systems* book cover. (Courtesy of John Wiley & Sons, 1999)

given at the University of Santa Clara in the early 1960s. I considered upgrading that write-up into book form, but it did not take very long to realize the considerable progress had been made beyond those notes. My area of interest, also, had shifted from fundamental academic studies to dealing with complex systems such as nuclear power plants.

I took advantage of my recent work on scaling, severe accidents, and review of computer system codes to produce the book with the cover shown in Figure 7-11. A full draft of the book was prepared and submitted to the well-known scientific/technical publisher John Wiley & Sons for review and acceptance. Wiley suggested extending the reactor methodology to another complex system, and the topic of global climate change is covered in the last chapter of the book. Interestingly, based on my nuclear power tendency to "err on the side of safety," I would favor applying practical corrective actions that can be taken now while monitoring the trend of global temperatures. "That is the conservative and appropriate way to proceed." I am especially proud of the organization of information of material presented for countercurrent flooding mechanisms and critical flow. Few copies of the book have been sold for graduate studies since its publication in 1999, but those limited sales do not detract from the great satisfaction I had in writing it. I refer to the book occasionally and when I do, I still wonder how the job got done.

EIGHT

S. LEVY INCORPORATED

S. Levy Incorporated (SLI) was formed, as noted in Chapter 7, in late 1977 and it was sold to Scientech LLC on December 4, 1998. The company operated with a single employee during its first year, grew to a peak of 60 employees in the mid- to late 1980s, and was sold in 1998 with about 30 persons on the payroll. SLI's primary function was to provide consulting services to the nuclear industry. SLI did not have a marketing organization and most of its contracts were the result of previous connections, satisfaction on prior completed projects, or recommendations. Only a few typical cases are covered in this chapter to illustrate SLI's scope of work and its capability.

Due to its location about 20 minutes away from the Electrical Power Research Institute (EPRI), a large portion (up to 40 percent) of SLI's work came from EPRI. Many of the contracts involved safety and reactor analysis and that subject area is covered first in this chapter under the EPRI subheading. Another important SLI involvement with EPRI was in the development of advanced light water reactor requirements and that subject is covered next. Other selective EPRI contracts are summarized in the last part of the EPRI section. With respect to industry involvement, the chapter deals first with the largest study SLI received to evaluate Brown & Root engineering when its contract on the South Texas Project was canceled. This was a major undertaking employing many retired GE engineers. Licensing and design basis services to the U.S. nuclear industry as well as training and other specialty areas are also discussed. The third portion of this chapter is devoted to international work, and its last and fourth part covers SLI's efforts to diversify away from nuclear power as well as the reasons for its lack of success in that endeavor.

EPRI SUPPORT

SAFETY AND REACTOR ANALYSIS

After the TMI-2 accident, it became clear that *operators of nuclear power plants should be able to analyze the steady-state and transient behavior of their plants to ensure safe operating conditions.* This required the development of an integrated and validated computer code package that covered a wide range of analyses, ranging from fuel cycle economics to operating transients and a specified set of accidents. The *EPRI Reactor Analysis Support Package* (RASP) met that objective.

> Operators of nuclear power plants should be able to analyze the steady-state and transient behavior of their plants to ensure safe operating conditions.

SLI had an important role in the formulation of RASP under the guidance of EPRI's Lance Agee. EPRI NP-4498, Volume 1, edited by John Sorensen of SLI, offers an introduction and overview of RASP, while the remaining Volumes 2 through 9 identify items for utility users to consider in their modeling and analyses. They include PWR and BWR event guidelines, PWR and BWR physics guidelines, setpoint analysis and methodology, and BWR stability analysis. With RASP, utilities were able to analyze fuel reload patterns and plant design changes to satisfy their technical specifications and licensing basis.

The large role of SLI in RASP's development can be confirmed by the number of SLI engineers involved in its generation. Alphabetically, Ron Engel, Ed Fuller, Jim Healzer, Larry Keller, Al Ostenso, John Sorensen, and Gerry Walke are listed as coauthors of one or several volumes of RASP. In addition, SLI engineers were involved in the development of individual computer codes and their documentation, validation, and application. For example, Russ Mosteller had a dominant role in the overall physics code package, referred to as ARMP, which was used to follow the reactor core behavior, to optimize fuel cycles, and to generate thermal-hydraulic inputs. Dr. Mosteller was an excellent physicist, cognizant of advances in his field and a participant in most technical nuclear physics meetings. Dr. Larry Eisenhart developed a three-dimensional code, ARROTTA, that coupled reactor physics and thermal hydraulics. In other instances, SLI engineers supported the needs of the computer codes: John Hench and Jay Gillis developed an EPRI BWR critical heat flux correlation; Jim Healzer and Davood Abdollahian developed NATBWR, a natural circulation model to evaluate BWR power decreases when the water level was reduced during an anticipated transient without scram (ATWS); and Randy May developed a compact analyzer for BWR applications.

The RASP package was supported by other contractors who developed the VIPRE code for thermal-hydraulics predictions and the RETRAN code for plant transient analyses. In particular, the RETRAN system code had superior balance of plant simulation. Also, over the years, it moved from single-point kinetics to one- and two-dimensional kinetics.

The RASP package had one shortcoming: It was not able to predict the loss-of-coolant accident (LOCA). EPRI and its members preferred to rely on the vendors for those predictions because the models needed to be upgraded as results became available from the large LOCA test programs being carried out at that time. Also, the national laboratories were developing excellent LOCA system computer codes such as TRAC, RELAP, and BWR-TRAC, which were available to all users. In many ways, SLI acted as an extension of EPRI during this period of developing tools to predict the performance of nuclear power plants. SLI engineers were knowledgeable and experienced because they had performed similar work for GE and utilities. Note that it was SLI's policy not to pursue any GE hiring until the engineer involved had approached SLI and firmly decided to leave his or her current employment.

ADVANCE LIGHT WATER REACTOR REQUIREMENTS

In the early to mid-1980s, the Nuclear Power Division of EPRI sponsored an industry-wide program to develop an advance light water reactor (ALWR) requirements document for future nuclear power plants. The lack of new nuclear orders for nearly 10 years led to the formulation of a program with the objectives of improved safety, enhanced plant performance, reduced cost, and regulatory stabilization. The program participants included the nuclear utilities, the NRC, reactor system suppliers, architect-engineers, and consulting engineers. Utility, regulatory, and industry experience with current operating plants was to be used in formulating the requirements.

I was fortunate to be able to go with John Taylor, director of EPRI's Nuclear Division, Dr. Karl Stahlkopf, who was to initially manage the program, Larry Minnick, and Lou Martel, who arranged the meetings, to visit several utility officers and to hear their complaints about their operating plants and their perceptions about desirable changes. The most common objection was that the *nuclear power plants had become more and more complicated and that they should be simplified.* The emergency diesel generators and the need to test them to the point that they may not start up when needed were criticized universally. Several plant managers suggested the possibility of starting from a fresh piece of paper. Utilities who shared ownership of their plants to get the cost benefit of increased output showed a preference for plants of reduced size to avoid accommodating different state regulations. There were many concerns about the continued increase in the number of regulations and in the extended time required to get a license. The result of those visits was summarized in an EPRI Report, RP 1585, "Summary of Discussions with Utilities and Preferred Characteristics of New LWRs" which I coauthored with L. Martel and L. Minnick. Based on those findings, the decision was made to proceed along two parallel paths:

- Apply proven technology, components, and systems but simplify the current plants by reducing the number of systems and

components and the time required for construction. Plant operability, availability, and maintainability were to be enhanced as
well as plant resistance to severe accidents.

- Develop a plant having a reduced output of about 600 MWe with
passive features such as natural circulation in a BWR and grav-
ity-driven safety systems to remove decay heat and to respond to
accidents.

The NRC agreed to review the requirements document and to certify
the plant designs using them. As a result, NUREG-1197 was issued
by the NRC to describe their program management and staff review
methodology and it acknowledges the support of EPRI managers and
the efforts of SLI licensing engineer Ron Engel. The NRC review was
carried out through a series of quarterly meetings with the NRC Policy
Committee dating from August 1983 to March 1986 and a large number
of working staff meetings. The requirements documentation consisted
of 13 chapters, which were scheduled to reach the NRC from July 1986
to September 1988 with all the reviews completed by June 1989.

GE also submitted its advance boiling water reactor (ABWR) with
internal recirculation pumps for certification while Combustion
Engineering (CE) proceeded with their improved System 80 plus, which
they had sold to South Korea. Westinghouse decided to pursue a passive
600-MWe PWR (AP600), and GE initiated the development of their
simplified BWR (SBWR) using natural circulation.

The funds for this work were shared between DOE and industry.
Several foreign countries such as Japan, South Korea, and Holland were
interested and participated in the work and funding. This was a large
undertaking that was managed by EPRI under the guidance of a Utility
Steering Committee. EPRI used two consulting firms to help their
management of the program: SLI and MPR & Associates, which acted
as staff extensions of EPRI project management. The two consulting
firms subdivided the responsibility for chapters in the report according
to the talent and capability of their personnel. At SLI, Ron Engel, Lee
Fidrych, Tom Fukushima, Chuck Johnson, Roy Jones, and Don Scapini
participated in the work. The approach used was to have a draft of each

chapter prepared and sent for review and comments by the utilities and all involved contractors. A chapter revision was prepared and a meeting held to resolve the comments. Because of personnel turnover, the same questions were raised several times and SLI agreed to create a database of all the issues raised and their resolution. Lee Fidrych was in charge of that database.

A special Test and Analysis Group was also formed to review the development programs and new analyses planned for the two passive plants, AP-600 and SBWR. The group was chaired by my good friend Tom Fernandez, who started at GE and EPRI, spent several years at Yankee Atomic, and then rejoined the EPRI staff. The group members were Doug Chapin from MPR, Nick Trikouros from GPUN, and the author. Periodic meetings were held with Westinghouse and GE, meeting minutes were prepared, and comments and recommendations kept open until they were resolved satisfactorily. Oral presentations of the group's progress were made by Tom Fernandez to the Utility Steering Committee. The group's decision to insist on an AP-600 thermal-hydraulic test simulation received a lot of attention until the NRC reached the same conclusion.

Another debated area was the need for tests of the SBWR containment. Tests were performed at the Paul Scherrer Institut in Switzerland and Jim Healzer of SLI participated in that work. The completion of the test and analysis program was important to the certification of AP-600 by the NRC. In the case of the SBWR, its certification review was not completed because GE decided that a 600-MWe output would not be competitive and increased its size to 1000 MWe, which disappointed both DOE and EPRI and stopped their support of the SBWR. It is interesting to note that the latest passive plants, AP-1000 and ESBWR, are planning to operate at or above 1000 MWe.

The requirements document satisfied current regulatory basis and such other licensing guidance as the Standard Review Plan. It also met the resolution of generic issues. The review process, documented in NUREG-1197, is reproduced in Figure 8.1 and it allowed plant optimization subjects, developed as alternatives by EPRI to current regulatory requirements, to be introduced after review and acceptance by the NRC.

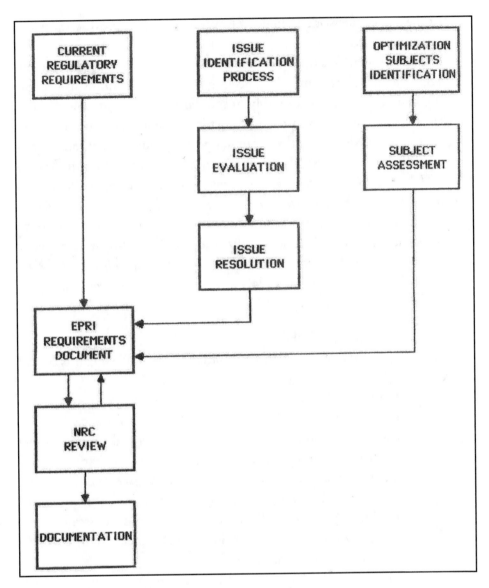

Figure 8.1.   The NUREG-1197 review process for the ALWR.
(Source: NUREG-1197, 1986)

At the end of the work, a single SER was issued by the NRC with evaluations provided for each chapter.

The requirements document employed a special format with side-by-side "Requirements" and "Engineering Rationale" columns to become the first and complete assembly of standards for nuclear power plants agreed to by all involved parties. This formidable task could not have been completed without the strong support and guidance of John Taylor of EPRI. *It was remarkable to see previous competitors sit down at the same table and reach agreement for the simple reason that there was no market to compete for and no chance for competitive collusion.* Even though the requirements document was not put to use to build new nuclear power plants, it is certain to help standardize the design of future nuclear plants and to improve their performance. *The document also offers considerable and valuable advice about how to proceed in the future to avoid some of the problems discussed in Chapter 6.*

OTHER EPRI SUPPORT

SLI participated in many other EPRI projects. The following lists typical cases:

- SLI kept a database of industry fuel failures and coolant chemistry. Wayne Michaels and Mary McKenna of SLI kept the database, which was used to develop a computer code to successfully predict the number of fuel failures from radioactivity measurements at the power plants; *the water chemistry database showed that chloride was a major contributor to steam generator tube denting,* but it failed to predict other modes of failure of steam generator tubes due to inconsistencies and deficiencies in the collected water chemistry information.
- In the NSAC-21 report, SLI developed a *fundamental safety parameter set for boiling water reactors,* which was used in designing BWR safety parameter display systems.
- A critical flow data review was carried out and it showed that the large pipe failure tests at Marviken could be predicted by available models. A homogeneous nonequilibrium critical flow model was developed. A calculation methodology was generated

for leak rates through cracks in pipes and tubes. A two-phase jet model was formulated and utilized to determine jet loadings.

- A review of proposed containment improvements was carried out, including filtering/venting of BWR pressure suppression and PWR ice containments, as well as a feasibility study of a novel self-actuated pressure relief device invented by Larry Minnick for nuclear reactor containments.

- Drs. T. L. Gerber and Y. S. Garud of SLI participated in EPRI studies of intergranular stress corrosion cracking of Ni-Cr-Fe alloy 600 tubes in PWR primary water review and the assessments for model development.

- Under the ALWR requirements program, SLI carried out a joint EPRI-CRIEPI joint assessment of BWR passive plant heat removal. Early recovery of the decay heat removal system was also examined to prevent severe accidents.

- Gerry Walke of SLI was responsible for the quality assurance of the EPRI hydrogen burning tests performed in Las Vegas, while Drs. Jay Gillis and Jim Healzer developed a model to predict hydrogen release rates during different types of severe accidents.

- S. Levy had a continued involvement in the review of the Modular Accident Analysis Program (MAAP) for severe accident analyses and he participated in the development of the *Severe Management Guidance Report.*

In retrospect, SLI benefited greatly from EPRI work because it provided a good and stable base of support to compensate for the ups and downs in industry subcontracts. The EPRI investigations were novel and challenging and the proximity to EPRI assured EPRI project managers access to SLI personnel and to myself if SLI work was behind schedule or unsatisfactory. The response was immediate, but fortunately the number of such calls was very small. SLI owes its success in many ways to EPRI and this book gives me an opportunity to thank my many friends and coworkers at EPRI.

INDUSTRY SUPPORT

BROWN & ROOT ENGINEERING ON THE SOUTH TEXAS PROJECT

SLI was asked to study and evaluate Brown & Root (B&R) engineering work on the South Texas Project (STP). Houston Lighting & Power Company (HL&P) was the principal owner of STP and, along with co-owners, had instigated a lawsuit surrounding the B&R work. SLI was asked by HL&P:

- "To examine the status of B&R's engineering and design versus time and to assess how well B&R met its engineering and design completion commitments.

- To determine whether B&R engineering supported construction needs and to what degree B&R engineering contributed to delays of the STP project.

- To establish whether B&R's design and engineering work was carried out in accordance with normal professionally accepted standards.

- To assess the management, organization, and planning of B&R engineering. The capability of key managers and lead discipline engineers was to be evaluated as well as their interfaces with other functions.

- To review the adequacy of B&R's engineering, both in terms of the process used to carry out the work and the technical quality of the output. Where SLI found deficiencies, their cause was to be established whenever possible.

- To provide an independent assessment based upon the above studies of B&R's capability to complete the engineering of STP and of the decision to replace B&R with another Architect/Engineer."

To meet those objectives, SLI carried out detailed studies of B&R engineering in 29 specific areas covering systems, structures, and components critical to plant safety, operation, and schedule completion. In each instance, the history, timeliness, quality, and adequacy of B&R work were examined and the principal engineering problems were identified as well as the major changes made by Bechtel after turnover. In addition, separate studies of the B&R engineering organization, personnel capability, nuclear experience, and turnover were completed as well as a thorough examination of engineering progress reports to top B&R responsible management.

SLI was fortunate to have access to the large number of plant records, which must be preserved by law, the B&R internal and STP files, the Bechtel proposed changes to STP and their justifications, and the enormous amount of deposition material generated by the lawsuit. That information allowed SLI to produce a report, Volumes I and II, 546 pages long, containing very incriminating evidence, including a very large number of supportive quotations from B&R files.

In retrospect, the dominant reason for B&R problems was their inexperience with engineering nuclear power plants. The South Texas Project was their first order and they did not have the engineering capability or talent to produce the unique and rigorous information required. Construction proceeded with low completion of engineering, which led to delays and hardware modifications due to rework. Control of engineering documents was poor and there were problems with quality control.

> In retrospect, the dominant reason for B&R problems was their inexperience with engineering nuclear power plants.

I was in charge of the B&R evaluation and I was assured by Jack Newman (an independent lawyer who was involved in the lawsuit and had recommended SLI for the study) that the legal team would not force its legal opinions on SLI engineers. As expected, Jack kept his word, but lawyers for some minority owners kept insisting on strengthening the text of the final reports without justification. For that reason, I did not allow any change to the SLI reports without my approval. Another reason was that I expected to be the principal witness at the trial and I did not want to be surprised by any statement in the reports. The SLI reports were introduced as evidence and a significant monetary settlement was reached without a trial. The study offered several lessons learned:

1. SLI employed many retired GE engineers during the study and they really enjoyed working again. The quality of their engineer-

ing was excellent. *The use of such retirees should be given serious consideration if and when new nuclear orders occur in order to reduce the potential shortage of experienced engineers.*

2. The differences in nuclear power plant capability between an experienced and an inexperienced architect-engineer can be enormous and cannot be compensated by favorable contractual terms.

3. Litigation work is interesting, but not challenging technically. While it was enjoyable to reconstruct the many ups and downs in B&R's engineering progress and to make several trips to the site to see the construction rework, it cannot match developing a new design or analysis.

4. Litigation work can generate good profits especially if the organization can be augmented by happy and capable retirees. It has one important shortcoming: The work can be stopped without notice and without enough time to get work for the released engineers.

5. One minority owner lawyer tried to get SLI to support a lawsuit against HL&P, which was turned down right away. That incident, also, convinced me to decline participation in any future litigation work.

After the STP settlement with B&R, SLI was asked to carry out a review program of the STP litigation between the City of Austin (COA) and HL&P. COA was a minority owner of STP. The purpose of the review was to

... determine whether the litigation discloses any previously unidentified safety-related deficiency in the systems, structures, or components of STP or their associated design or quality documents and to document the findings in a retrievable form. To do this, record documents containing factual information relating to technical aspects of the design and construction—that is, trial transcripts, deposition transcripts, and documents designated by the parties before the trial as potential trial exhibits or as exhibits during the trial—were reviewed.

This review was carried out in three phases. Phase I dealt with the pretrial record up to July 25, 1988. Phase II covers the pretrial record created up to January 16, 1989. Phase III completed the litigation review and included materials filed with the court but not previously reviewed.

For each phase, HL&P first determined which documents might contain information about technical aspects and transmitted such material to SLI for detailed review. Next, SLI performed a detailed, line-by-line review of all documents identified during the screening process. In addition, for Phase III, 15,000 pages of trial transcripts were reviewed at the STP site. During these reviews, each assertion describing a deficiency was recorded and the assertions analyzed to see if they were safety related, erroneous, previously identified, or resolved. For instance, under Phase III, 460 assertions were identified and they did not disclose any previously unrecognized safety-related deficiencies. The work of identifying and analyzing assertions was performed by engineers experienced in the nuclear power industry, including a number specifically knowledgeable about design and construction of STP. *Most engineers involved felt that the litigation process was rather voluminous, tedious, and quite inefficient.* Chuck Johnson of SLI was in charge of this project, while Jack Bailey of HL&P was responsible for its management.

The conduct of the Litigation Record Review Program was controlled by plans and procedures. A senior advisory panel reviewed the plans and results of each phase. The program was also monitored by SLI Quality Assurance staff. It was audited by the NRC at its start and twice by HL&P Nuclear Assurance personnel. It has resulted in a completely auditable record, consisting of hardcopy files, a computerized database, and final reports for each phase. The HL&P quality assurance personnel will remember this litigation record review because they had the scare of their life when they were at the SLI offices the day of the large earthquake which collapsed several Bay Area overpasses and damaged the Bay Bridge. After rushing to the SLI parking lot, they decided to return to their hotel to deal with the aftershocks. They did not show up the following day because they decided to catch the first flight going back to Texas where the audit was completed rather than risk another "shaking" trip to Northern California.

INDUSTRY SERVICES

LICENSING SERVICES

Ed Fuller was the second in command for licensing at GE when he decided to join SLI. Ed knew the utility licensing personnel as well as the lawyers supporting them. Ed started by accepting assignments for his services at power plants. Next, he was able to place such other SLI licensing engineers as Sid Smith and Larry Keller at other plants that did not want to hire permanent employees to meet the increased licensing workload generated by the TMI-2 accident. Two other SLI licensing engineers, Bruce Lacy and Billy Reid, were relocated to Iowa to service the Duane Arnold plant.

This "body-shop" type work was pursued by SLI only if the engineers involved agreed to it. Also, the persons involved continued to attend company business meetings to remain informed about progress and future plans for the company. Ed Fuller, who became a vice president of SLI shortly after joining it, was in charge of this work until he decided to leave SLI to form his own consulting firm. His departure was friendly and his shares in SLI were repurchased over time. A no-compete agreement was not signed, because SLI's good lawyer, Henry Bose, felt that it would not be enforceable. Ed and I have remained good friends and continued to bet on the Stanford–Berkeley annual football games for many years.

Ron Engel was another GE licensing engineer who decided to join SLI. His name was mentioned previously under the EPRI ALWR requirements document discussion. Ron was very capable and preferred to stay at his home base to produce original licensing documents. For example, he prepared a generic reload licensing document that established reload characteristics, which, if satisfied, would eliminate the submittal of a reload licensing report to the NRC before each refueling. Submittal of a letter showing satisfaction of the generic requirements would allow the plant to proceed. Ron was much more an individual contributor than a manager and all the SLI licensing engineers previously mentioned, reporting to Ed Fuller, sought his advice when necessary. Certain utilities liked Ron's licensing output so much that he was kept very busy.

DESIGN BASIS SERVICES

After the design basis of the Millstone, Connecticut, plants was found not to have been kept up to date, the NRC sought assurance that other operating plants could satisfy their licensing basis. This led to significant opportunities to restore plant design bases, and SLI was able to capture a limited fraction of that work by offering a novel cost reduction if allowed to use its output on more than one plant.

> The problem with "design basis" was the lack of a clear definition of the documents to satisfy it.

The problem with "design basis" was the lack of a clear definition of the documents to satisfy it. The volume of paper generated to get an operating license was enormous and the intent was not to update it all; *only the critical characteristics in documents essential to the safe operation of the plant needed to be kept up to date.* It is hoped that future plants will generate such a list, use a means to identify the critical information, and reduce the number of documents where it appears. Also, since the Final Safety Analysis Report (FSAR) defines the licensing basis, I have suggested several times that it should be a controlled document using underlining or bold printing of areas critical to safety, but the owners have declined consistently to do so, most likely due to the large number of pages in a typical FSAR submittal. *With the new information systems available, it should be easier to define and keep up to date the licensing basis and the plant critical characteristics.* I hope that new nuclear power plants can solve this problem once and for all.

CONTROL AND INSTRUMENTATION SERVICES

The first SLI entry in the control and instrumentation (C&I) field was developed by John Hench, who went to the TMI-2 plant to assist the Industry Advisory Group. While at the plant, he convinced himself that the accident could have been avoided with guidance to the operators from measurements at the plant. In fact, John had invented an *initial version of the safety parameter display system (SPDS) and applied for a patent of his design.* It was granted by the U.S. Patent Office and it was expanded to cover Japan with the financial support of Toshiba who decided to build a first version of that invention. Tom Fukushima, one of SLI's hardest working engineers, was dispatched to Japan to get the prototype built. During my visit to Japan for another reason, I visited with Tom and Toshiba personnel and found that Toshiba was happy with the idea and the progress being made.

As an aside, when Tom and I went to lunch, I was surprised by the discrimination shown to Tom by the waitress. She took my order in English while refusing to do the same for Tom because she was convinced that he was Japanese and trying to show off by using English. Tom was born in the United States and could not speak any Japanese, but the waitress kept talking to him in Japanese, trying to force him to do the same. She also brought his lunch long after mine. It was fortunate that Tom was a very patient engineer.

In the meantime, John Hench was able to convince *Pennsylvania Power & Light (PP&L) to give SLI the order for their SPDS at the Susquehanna plants.* One reason was that the GE shops were overloaded and could not meet their schedule. Another reason was that SLI was willing to customize the design to fit PP&L desires. SLI saw the order as an opportunity to break into a new hardware business and the *decision was made to build a full prototype and to test hardware and software before shipment to the plants.*

Such testing became possible because SLI had decided to move from rented space to a new SLI-owned office building, which was designed with a computer test room and a false floor to accommodate cable pulling. This was a full quality assurance project and the SLI team performed quite well. SLI also found out that additional orders could not be obtained once GE decided to develop a standard design and get the benefit of volume production. At that time, SLI notified nuclear systems suppliers of the SLI patent and asked them to take it into account. SLI received no response and decided not to pursue its legal rights, expecting to be outmatched in funds and legal support.

SLI continued to be interested in C&I work and John Hench and his team went after non-nuclear, energy-saving applications, as discussed later. There was a small group of GE engineers who had left the company to provide independent training services and consultation in C&I. They were located in Morgan Hill, California, about 20 miles south from SLI offices. They approached SLI about the possibility of joining the firm and an agreement was reached. They were very good at providing training services and I received several letters of appreciation about their teaching and training material. The new group failed to remain profitable when more plant owners staffed their facilities with their own instructors. To break even, the group decided to design and install C&I hardware at nuclear power plants, but the costs of such contracts were underestimated and SLI found out that they could not compete against the nuclear systems suppliers and their marketing organizations.

OTHER INDUSTRY SERVICES

SLI participated in a variety of other services programs. For instance, Al Klose and Wayne Michaels were involved in a program to *inspect fuel at the Surry Nuclear Power Station, to remove defective fuel rods, and to insert dummy fuel rods.* This was a joint effort with KraftWerk Union (KWU) of Germany.

Another project deserving of mention is the study of *Rancho Seco Nuclear Generation Station nuclear fuel storage options* in which I participated with H. Klepfer, J. Heald, and S. Smith with the support of R. Jones and J. Friscia. The final report evaluated a total of 15 options and recommended continued storage in the spent fuel pool followed by storage in transportable casks to be supported in their development by DOE funds. That choice was made because it could lead to early acceptance of the spent fuel by DOE or an early shipment to a storage facility. I declined remuneration to be deposited about that report because it allowed me to defend the report without being influenced by the parties involved in a lawsuit. At a deposition in the SMUD versus the DOE lawsuit, I found out how bad my loss of memory was because I could not remember the name of any person working on that subject at Rancho Seco.

In retrospect, SLI Services were in demand when the plant owners wanted an independent review or assessment or when SLI developed a special niche or had a novel idea or a new solution to a field problem.

The following are typical cases:
- SLI supported plant owners trying to develop their own reactor and safety analysis. Independent reviews were carried out when a new fuel vendor was selected for a reload or when its analysis was being questioned by the NRC.
- C. Johnson and Al Ostenso were the first to explain an anomaly in water level BWR measurements by realizing that the water level pressure lines contained trapped air because the line installation was not always declining toward the reactor vessel.
- When the Shoreham plant in Long Island was shut down with very little exposure of its core, Al Klose contacted several BWR owners to consider the use of that fuel in their plants. PECO was the only owner interested and an agreement was made to ship the fuel from Shoreham to Limerick with great savings to both owners.
- SLI performed evaluations or reviews of nuclear organizations, including the management review of Northeast Utilities Nuclear Engineering Department (with Theodore Barry & Associates), the evaluation of the Corporate Nuclear Safety Section for Carolina Power & Light Company, and the evaluation of the Safety Committee of Consolidated Edison Company of New York.

INTERNATIONAL SALES

SLI received a limited number of international contracts. Good relations had been established with Toshiba while at GE and their top management would stop at SLI offices whenever they visited GE at San Jose. Toshiba also gave SLI a contract to produce progress reports about the U.S. licensing status and to prepare write-ups on special topics they selected. During their study of improved BWR designs, they asked Dr. Jay Gillis of SLI to perform tests on jet pumps at Stanford University to improve the pump efficiency. Our largest contracts in Japan came from independent fuel vendors trying to improve their thermal-hydraulics predictions. Jim Healzer and John Sorensen of SLI handled those requests.

Another good international customer was the Leibstadt plant in Switzerland where Al Klose had very good relations with their top managers. At their request, SLI procured a pump from a canceled U.S. plant, had it modified by Byron-Jackson and delivered on time. Also, Dr. Randy May and his young graduating engineers used artificial intelligence to try to instruct operators about actions to be taken to remain within a plant's technical specifications.

SLI's international work again relied on contacts and reputation. *In retrospect, to increase the international sales volume, it would have been necessary to have local marketing operations close to the customer offices. SLI's amount of sales could not support that overhead increase—which some other consultants found out too late.*

> In retrospect, to increase the international sales volume, it would have been necessary to have local marketing operations close to the customer offices.

SLI'S GROWTH AND DIVERSITY

NON-NUCLEAR SALES

In 1993–1994, nuclear power plant costs were excessive and their owners tried to reduce them. Consulting contracts were the first to suffer and SLI decided to diversify. John Hench decided to pursue means to *reduce energy costs in large refrigerated warehouses.* With the help of Tom Fukushima and Al Ostenso, a control system was designed to keep warehouse temperatures relatively constant and avoid undershoots and overshoots. The system worked, energy was saved, and the idea was extended to trucks transporting perishable goods. Next, it was applied to hatcheries and wineries where a constant temperature helped production and product quality.

A small separate business, with its own sales force, was set up and run by John Hench. Its profit and loss picture was tracked separately and the business losses increased when orders favored distributed controllers, which were less costly than the SLI integrated control system. Another reason was that *SLI overhead costs were too high for the new energy saving business.* So, SLI met its remaining sales obligations, reduced its marketing efforts, and eventually abandoned this first attempt at non-nuclear sales while John Hench started his own distributed control system energy-saving company.

Because of SLI's success in developing nuclear computer system codes, the decision was made to *enter engineering software sales for personal computers* (PCs). SLI's first product was software developed by Professor Bill Kays of Stanford University to design compact heat exchangers. SLI assumed responsibility for advertising and selling the software as well as answering customer questions. Dr. Jay Gillis handled those sales well and even extended the software to cover two-phase flow.

Our next effort was to be first with a PC version of a finite element code available on large computers and called LIBRA. With the agreement of the LIBRA owner, Ken Watkins of SLI was put in charge of LIBRA conversion to PCs. The process took more time than scheduled and the software was not user friendly. To help its usage, a preprocessor was added but it reached the market after several other superior entries became available. When LIBRA and its preprocessor were ready, the number of sales was too small to justify continued support. SLI also developed software to predict the thermodynamic properties of steam and other gases. The surprise finding, in this case, was that *engineers would not spend their money to acquire such computer aids unless their company purchased them.* Also, several university professors were developing similar software and undercutting SLI prices.

SLI's last try at the software business was back under the nuclear scope when it decided to purchase a PC power plant computer code developed by Dr. Parveen Jain who was an outstanding programmer. The user-friendly *software used plant measurements to detect loss of performance and suggest maintenance or other actions to correct the deficiencies.* The code was purchased by several utilities and an owners' group was formed to determine needed improvements. Unfortunately, the number of participants decreased as the power plant owners pursued cost reduction programs. Jain wanted to develop a more powerful control system PC code, but SLI and Jain disagreed on its projected profitability and a friendly separation was worked out. *In retrospect, the proposed plant control system would have been very useful if the required instrumentation had been developed and could be maintained readily.*

There were many reasons for SLI's lack of success in the non-nuclear business. In contrast to its nuclear involvement—where SLI knew its customers, understood their needs, and had knowledgeable engineers capable of responding to them—SLI did not know its non-nuclear customers and it did not have the marketing skills to reach them. Furthermore, a constraint was imposed on the new businesses. The money available for their pursuit was limited by an established objective of maintaining a break-even balance sheet for the entire company. In spite of those difficulties, SLI came close to penetrating a few new businesses and the engineers involved enjoyed their exposure to new fields.

> In retrospect, the proposed plant control system would have been very useful if the required instrumentation had been developed and could be maintained readily.

MANAGEMENT OF SLI

I did not spend much time managing the company because it was staffed with senior engineers capable of looking after their own contracts. Shortly after its formation, Jim Healzer, Ed Fuller, and John Hench joined SLI in that order. They were elected vice presidents and allowed to purchase 12.5 percent of the company shares. I owned 62.5 percent of the company and remained the largest shareholder until the company was sold. The company had a good financial tracking system, which provided monthly reports on every contract, application rate of every employee, and results by organization groups.

Except for the last three to four years, SLI was profitable every year. Half of the profits were applied to retirement benefits and the other half saved for future business growth. The company had excellent benefit plans. From the start, the retirement fund was managed by an investment firm receiving guidance from three SLI engineers selected by all the employees. This plan limited SLI future commitments and it was modified in later years to allow each employee to invest his or her own retirement funds.

> The emphasis at SLI was on overall company results rather than performance by each suborganization.

The emphasis at SLI was on overall company results rather than performance by each suborganization. Some employees were fully chargeable while others spent a fraction of their time getting contracts for themselves and other employees. That distribution was controlled by the overall company applied rate, which was kept at a level high enough for the company to be profitable. I relied on the applied rate tabulation to encourage the managers to increase the applied rate of some of their personnel or to use employees with low application in other suborganizations.

As the number of fixed-price contracts increased with time, proposal meetings were held to review them and to discuss future opportunities. Regular staff meetings were held and company information sessions were scheduled for all employees to report results and future work. All employees received annual reviews and there was one holiday get-together for all employees and their families. I had an open-door policy and I tended to manage informally by walking around and talking to employees. Employees were allowed to establish their working plans on their own as long as they satisfied their contract commitments.

Because reports were the output of SLI, an outstanding staff handled that work very well. They could edit the material to be typed and they could even read my handwriting. There was an administrator who managed the staff, handled medical bills, negotiated health and insurance contracts, obtained clearance for SLI personnel to visit power plant sites, and handled my calls when I traveled. There was a finance manager and a staff of two to pay bills and employee salaries, review expense accounts, handle audits, and prepare monthly reports to be distributed to the staff. With that strong a staff, very few issues rose to my level and it allowed me to be highly applied.

Because the office lease charge kept increasing, I decided that SLI should have its own building and I put Al Klose in charge of that project. SLI entered into a sharing agreement with a well-known San Jose builder, Barry Swanson. After three years of joint ownership, SLI

Figure 8.2.   SLI's San Jose headquarters. (Source: S. Levy Incorporated)

had the right to purchase Swanson's half of the partnership, which SLI did. SLI used an architect to design a two-story, Spanish-style building with a hockey stick appearance. It was subdivided into separate offices, each with a window and occupied by one engineer. An early outside picture of the building is reproduced in Figure 8.2. Initially SLI occupied 70 percent of the building and leased the rest. There was some opposition to investing SLI's hard-earned profits in a building, but with the escalating California real estate prices, it turned out to be the best investment by far ever made by SLI.

SALE OF SLI

I had always intended to leave the SLI business to its employees, and an Employees Stock Ownership Plan was established to buy 30 percent of my shares. The value of the shares was established by a formula developed by an outside accounting firm, which discounted the business value by 20 percent because it was held privately. When I reached age 65, Dr. Harold Klepfer was appointed president and chief operating officer, while I retained the titles of chairman of the board and chief executive officer. Harold managed to make a slight profit in his first year of presidency but he was not able to break even in the following year. SLI initiated a search for a new president and ended up hiring Joe Famiglietti, who had been recommended by a consulting firm. Joe had run a much larger consulting firm for Combustion Engineering (CE) and he became available when CE decided to sell its consulting business.

I had moved away from the SLI building because several employees kept bypassing Klepfer to come to me for a decision. Joe's management style was different from mine. It was much more formal and he asked for more accurate predictions of income from the employees every week. He wanted to grow the business and he was looking at potential mergers or joint ventures. The company losses increased because Joe's time and trips were not chargeable. Also, young key engineers were leaving the company to join the booming Silicon Valley firms at much higher salaries. Several key staffers saw little benefit to the detailed information Joe requested and they were ready to rebel and resign, forcing me to buy out the rest of Famiglietti's contract in 1995. A triumvirate was installed to manage SLI. It consisted of Ron Engel, Randy May, and Ed Fuller. That arrangement started smoothly, but friction developed and Ron Engel was eventually named president and Davood Abdollahian (the first UCB graduate hired by SLI) was named vice president to help with the administrative duties.

A few years earlier, I had tried to sell my shares to the Employee Stock Ownership Plan (ESOP) and a loan was secured from the Silicon Valley Bank to pay me off. However, SLI stopped being profitable and I decided not to proceed with the loan because of the risks of not satisfying all of the loan terms. My next try was to sell my shares to the ESOP, not to charge interest, and to be paid over many years taking into account SLI's future profitability. SLI's calculated share value was declining at that time and it became clear that SLI employees were not willing to acquire more SLI shares, so the ESOP administrators rejected my offer. At the next board meeting, plausible solutions were discussed, and the president, Ron Engel, suggested selling SLI. Al Klose put together a package of information about SLI and sent it to several potential buyers. Scientech LLC was the first to show an interest and it agreed to purchase SLI just for its receivables.

The next problem was to agree on a purchase price for the SLI shares owned by ESOP. It was necessary to put a price on the building value and an independent appraisal was obtained. After a few concessions on both sides, a share price was established at about twice the value calculated by the original SLI formula. The ESOP and other outstanding shares were paid off using the funds set aside for future SLI growth.

Scientech was not interested in the building and the ESOP could not own a building. Because Scientech wanted to retain the S. Levy Incorporated name, SLI sold its assets including the name and then changed its name to Peppertree Properties Inc., which was given the responsibility of running the SLI building. My daughter, Linda Smith, continued to do an excellent job of running the building. A lease agreement was signed with Scientech at a favorable rate to help the SLI personnel who had transferred to Scientech to remain profitable. Scientech expected to reach that goal by reducing staff and expenses as necessary rather than "spoiling the engineers" as SLI had done in the past. The staff at San Jose kept decreasing and soon nobody was left. After the sale of SLI, I created a fully owned business called Levy & Associates and I continued to operate as a single consultant to the nuclear industry. My office is now located in the old SLI building owned by Peppertree Properties. I go to the office every day to keep current with developments in nuclear power and to write this book as I head toward full retirement.

In retrospect, I learned that starting a business and growing it was easy compared to leaving it even though I was the majority owner. I enjoyed every minute at SLI and I felt very lucky to have had so many talented engineers and members of the staff working for me. I have continued to

In retrospect, I learned that starting a business and growing it was easy compared to leaving it.

operate as a single consultant and I look forward to being challenged as in the case of my most recent involvement in a short-term review of the draft *Global Nuclear Energy Partnership* (GNEP) for the Academy of Engineering. *Nuclear power is a most fascinating and challenging field that I recommend highly to new engineering students. I am glad to have spent my entire career doing whatever I could for both boiling and pressurized water reactors and I am proud of what has been accomplished when I look at their current safe and reliable performance.*

NINE

LESSONS LEARNED AND THE FUTURE GENERATION OF ELECTRICITY BY NUCLEAR POWER PLANTS

Hundred of lessons learned were identified in the preceding chapters. The purpose of this last chapter is to illustrate how some of the important retrospective findings can help the future nuclear generation of electricity. Three nuclear power plant categories are considered: (1) operating plants, (2) light water reactors to be built under the Nuclear Power 2010 Initiative (which evolved from *A Roadmap to Deploy New Nuclear Power Plants in the United States,* which was generated by the DOE and the nuclear industry and issued on October 31, 2001), and (3) future advanced reactors.

OPERATING PLANTS

The most important objective of currently operating nuclear power plants is to maintain their excellent safety and performance levels. For the last five years, the 103 light water–cooled U.S. nuclear plants have stayed online

> The most important objective of currently operating nuclear power plants is to maintain their excellent safety and performance levels.

over 90 percent of the time and their total production costs, including fuel, operations, and maintenance, have been well below the comparable costs of coal and natural gas power plants. Safety indicators of the operating plants have been very good as reported by the Nuclear Regulatory Commission (NRC) and the Institute of Nuclear Power Operations (INPO). The credit for those outstanding performance levels belongs to the plant owners-operators and the *strong leaders and motivators at the top of their nuclear programs* (see pages 116 and 129) who insist on a strong safety culture and the continued pursuit of excellence.

As noted in an earlier chapter, the term *safety culture* was introduced by the International Nuclear Safety Advisory Group (INSAG) of the International Atomic Energy Agency (IAEA) in their first report and expanded on in many subsequent INSAG reports. My preferred definition—most likely because I wrote it—is the one-page description of the characteristics of a good safety culture given on page 11 of INSAG-12, which is reproduced in Table 9.1. Most recently, the IAEA has built on previous publications and has issued a book titled *Safety Culture in the Maintenance of Nuclear Power Plants* (ISBN 92-041404). The NRC, also, just launched a safety culture initiative under the Reactor Oversight Program.

TABLE 9.1.   Characteristics of a Good Safety Culture (from INSAG-12)

— When any possible conflict in priority arises, safety and quality take precedence over schedule and cost.

— Errors and near misses when committed are seen not only as a matter of concern but also as a source of experience from which benefit can be derived. Individuals are encouraged to identify, report, and correct imperfections in their own work in order to help others as well as themselves to avert future problems.

— Plant changes or activities are conducted in accordance with procedures. If any doubt arises about the procedures, the evolution is terminated by returning the plant to a safe and stable condition. The procedures are evaluated and changed if necessary before proceeding further.

— When problems are identified, the emphasis is placed upon understanding the root cause of the problems and finding the best solutions without being diverted by who identified or contributed to the problem; the objective is to find "what is right" and not "who is right."

- The goal of supervisory and management personnel is that every task be done right the first time. They are expected to accept and insist upon full accountability for the success of each work activity and to be involved in the work to the extent necessary to achieve success.
- Practices and policies convey an attitude of trust and an approach that supports teamwork at all levels and reinforces positive attitudes towards safety.
- Feedback is solicited from station personnel and contractors to help identify concerns, impediments, and opportunities to improve.
- Management reinforces an attitude of individual behavior that leads staff to identify problems promptly and fully.
- The organization has a commitment to continuous safety improvement and to manage change effectively.
- Senior managers prevent isolationism and encourage the establishment of a learning organization.
- Every individual, every supervisor and every manager demonstrates personal integrity at every opportunity that arises during the lifetime of the nuclear power plant.
- Every plant change, every meeting and every safety assessment is taken as an opportunity to teach, learn, and reinforce the preceding characteristics and principles.
- These characteristics and principles are not compromised or relaxed.

During the Peach Bottom recovery, safety culture was described succinctly as *"the plan to have management and supervision assume their responsibilities to communicate, coach, and reinforce their expectations about how to operate Peach Bottom and to hold all employees accountable for their own words, and deeds"* (see page 123). Another way to judge a safety culture program is to check whether it can correct all the "troubled plant conditions" described on pages 113 to 142. A review of those pages shows that *the dominant*

The dominant cause of nuclear reactor problems was the failure to identify plant deficiencies and to correct them adequately.

cause of nuclear reactor problems was the failure to identify plant deficiencies and to correct them adequately. For example, see the following instances, some of which are paraphrased:

- Page 113 and 114: "many uncorrected equipment problems, several unanticipated shutdowns"
- Page 121: "several precursors overlooked and management not taking sufficient responsibility for their role in the crisis"
- Page 135: "many safety issues identified with no corrective actions being taken."

To be effective, safety culture must involve every member of the organization. For example, see:

- Page 117: "management not supportive of station staff identifying concerns and providing alternate views"
- Page 122: "no growth opportunity for operators."

By contrast, for benefits of staff involvement, see:

- Page 112: "maintenance ownership of plant led to improved INPO rating"
- Page 132: "introduction of a new culture and behavior in control room"

Finally, a good safety culture needs to avoid poor cost decisions, to keep up with industry changes, and to face plant aging problems. For example, see:

- Pages 108 and 139: "cutback in engineering to buy new steam generators impacted high backlog of design changes"; "profit site centers emphasizing cost reductions"
- Page 108: "no need to change and to adopt latest industry practices; no plan to cope with loss of experienced retiring personnel"
- Page 110: "inadequate ownership of training by plant management"
- Pages 45–46 and several times later: "inadequate materials performance and insufficient coolant chemistry control".

In summary, *operating plants need to continue to do what they have been doing well in the last five years: to identify new or repeated safety issues and to correct them fully; to deal with plant aging problems; and to plan for the retirement of experienced personnel and their replacement.*

LIGHT WATER REACTORS UNDER NUCLEAR POWER 2010 INITIATIVE

The most important goal of the new LWRs under the Nuclear Power 2010 Initiative is to achieve standardization of the design, procurement of equipment, and site construction. Prior attempts have been made to standardize in the United States but they have failed (see page 34) in contrast to success in other countries. The reason is that there will be 16 or more different U.S. owners of light water reactors under the Nuclear Power 2010 Initiative, whereas France, South Korea, and China have only one single owner. The U.S. companies' attitudes have changed and to date they have laid out a standardized approach to licensing.

> Operating plants need to continue to do what they have been doing well in the last five years: to identify new or repeated safety issues and to correct them fully; to deal with plant aging problems; and to plan for the retirement of experienced personnel and their replacement.

The companies have formed teams that are endorsing three designs: Westinghouse AP-1000, General Electric ESBWR, and AREVA EPR. Each team plans to use a *design-centered approach* to promote standardization from application to application. The number of architect-engineers (AEs) involved has not yet been specified. Also, *the most difficult issues of how to purchase the same critical components and how to proceed with similar construction remain to be resolved. They involve significant advance and progress payments and require reestablishing an entire infrastructure of facilities and personnel to produce the equipment and modules to ship to the sites. Arrangements still need to be worked out to gain the full benefits of standardization in procurement and construction.* Foreign suppliers may be available to help with the earliest orders, but they will have to use U.S. codes and standards or to show the equivalence of their own standards. Eventually, domestic production of most equipment and modules is preferable. But, it is not clear whether, for example, the pressure vessel and internals facilities illustrated in Figure 5.6, or comparable ones, are available or can be restored to production. Similar conditions prevail for pumps, valves, and control systems satisfying nuclear quality levels. *This issue will require satisfactory and early resolution.*

The retrospective suggests that many other lessons learned should be considered during the design, procurement, and construction of LWRs under the Nuclear Power 2010 Initiative. Typical examples, beyond those listed under Operating Plants, are given below:

- Pages 16 and 54: Avoid initial cost reductions at the expense of safety and reliability.
- Page 29: Comprehensive startup and power escalation program.
- Page 45: Total plant design increases possibility of standardization.
- Page 78: Avoid management by committee.
- Page 84: Limit changes by using a Configuration Control Board.
- Pages 95 and 140: Need for high completion of design (95 to 97 percent), assessment of major construction phase (86 percent complete), procurement of long lead items, fully integrated, logically linked, and resource loaded schedule, good budget with adequate contingency.
- Page 95: Strong project management and quality assurance.
- Pages 97: Need for stable and predictable regulatory process.
- Page 187: Good definition of design basis and ability to track it.
- Page 148: Good, factual, physics-based simulator for training operators.
- Page 149: Analysis of human/machine interactions before finalizing control room.
- Pages 148–149: Ability to predict steady, transient, and accident plant performance at site.
- Page 152: Use of risk-informed methodology .
- Page 180: Use of advanced light water requirements documents.

An obvious omission from that list is the staffing of all the new plants on top of replacing retirees from the operating plants. Also, the retrospective points out an important lesson learned at Peach Bottom, that is, *avoid favoring new plants over old plants* (see page 122 for a discussion of the Peach Bottom-Limerick situation).

In summary, the *new LWRs under the Nuclear Power 2010 Initiative need to standardize beyond the design stage and to build up a complete infrastructure to support them. Full advantage should be taken of all the lessons learned under the operating plants. Also, a very aggressive staffing program is necessary to support the new and the operating LWRs.*

> **Full advantage should be taken of all the lessons learned under the operating plants.**

FUTURE ADVANCED REACTORS

The United States is considering two advanced reactors: a very high temperature gas-cooled reactor to produce hydrogen and a liquid metal–cooled burner reactor to transmute transuranics separated from LWR spent fuel. The design of those advanced reactors is at the preliminary stage and joint international development programs are being formulated. Because both coolants have been used in the past, a thorough review of that past experience is essential to avoid past problems. For example, *the reliability of liquid metal to steam/water heat exchangers needs to be improved* (see page 14). Similarly, I had the opportunity to review the occurrence of vibrations and the resulting power decreases at the Fort St. Vrain gas cooled reactor located at Platteville, Colorado. They were produced by *flow-induced vibrations* and they can be very costly as previously noted for LWRs (see page 33). Consideration is being given to relying on a *vented containment* and some of the issues with venting were touched on in the case of the N Reactor (see pages 152–153).

Nearly all of the lessons learned listed under the Nuclear Power 2010 Initiative for LWRs apply to the advanced reactors. However, there are important differences in the years of experience and the status of development. LWR fuel is established fully, whereas the fuel development process for advanced reactors is just starting. Also, the water reactors are close to solving their materials and coolant chemistry issues, whereas the advanced reactors are beginning to deal with them at much increased temperatures. In many ways, one is reminded of the conditions prevailing at the start of LWR development, which is covered in Chapter 3. For example, see:

- Pages 12–13: Use the Naval Reactor Branch strategy to avoid surprises and to insist on getting the right answers, preferably from full-scale tests.
- Page 22: Construct and operate demonstration advanced reactors to ensure reliability and safety of operations of new features.
- Pages 4 and 148: Determine the correct physics and rely on them for predictions and simulator modeling.
- Pages 74 and 164: Use correct scaling of test facilities. (My preference has been to use the same coolant and conditions as the reactors and to employ full-length scaling in the flow direction to keep the time variable the same.)
- Pages 62–68 and page 126 on: Establish cause of fuel failures and their consequences especially for direct cycle gas or supercritical water-cooled reactors; assure very low probability of fuel failure during fabrication and irradiation.
- Page 75: Determine causes of material failure and their correction as well as presence of corrosion products in the coolant and their cleanup.

The preceding list is only illustrative of the needs of advanced reactors. Once the preliminary designs are determined, a complete development program can be formulated (see the Gen IV discussion in Chapter 7). It should cover nuclear physics, thermal hydraulics, safety analysis predictive tools, and tests of different fuels and materials at very high temperatures. Tests of novel equipment will have to be carried out, preferably at full scale, for example, for a direct cycle helium turbine. Also, the applicable severe accidents should be defined and a methodology developed for predicting their consequences. Finally, closing the fuel cycle should be given early consideration.

There are excellent opportunities for research and development, system and equipment design, safety analysis and licensing, equipment procurement, construction, and start-up tests, which should attract new engineering students to the field of advanced nuclear power plants. If I were 50 years younger, I know that I would jump at the chance to participate in that type of work because it would require engineers (1) to design correctly scaled test facilities, to correlate the test data, and to develop analytical predictions of the results; (2) to understand how advanced reactor systems and components interact safely with each other; (3) to avoid severe accidents and to mitigate their consequences; and (4) to validate all that work in reactor startup tests. *I hope many future engineering students will see the benefits of pursuing the continued growth of nuclear electricity generation and its contribution to the well-being of the entire world.*

> I hope many future engineering students will see the benefits of pursuing the continued growth of nuclear electricity generation and its contribution to the well-being of the entire world.